FAST REACTIONS

Fast Reactions

DAVID N. HAGUE
University of Kent

WILEY–INTERSCIENCE
A Division of John Wiley & Sons Ltd
LONDON NEW YORK SYDNEY TORONTO

Library of Congress Catalog Card No. 74–149571

ISBN 0 471 33900 8

Printed in Great Britain at the Pitman Press, Bath

PREFACE

Kinetics, as a discipline, is more than a hundred years old. Many experimental data have been collected and impressive theories have been constructed as a result, but classical kinetics was severely limited by the inability to follow reactions with half-periods of less than a few seconds. Moreover, these fast reactions include many of vital practical and theoretical importance. Muscle action, cell reproduction, the combustion of rocket fuel and gasolene and, perhaps on a more sinister plane, the actions of poisons and nerve gases—all of these involve reactions which are complete within a fraction of a second and would thus provide a truly formidable challenge to classical kinetics. But one of the most exciting scientific achievements has been the development in recent years of experimental techniques for studying the rapid chemical changes which are of such importance in nature and modern civilization.

The aim of this book is to present, in a way intelligible to senior undergraduates and to research workers, some of the ideas behind these techniques, an outline of the methods themselves and, equally important, some of the more significant reactivity patterns revealed by these studies. The latter are especially interesting because a complex phenomenon such as the mechanism of action of a particular enzyme can be thought of in terms of its elementary steps, and these can be correlated with the reactivity patterns established for more simple, well-defined chemical systems.

Inevitably, it has been necessary to concentrate on certain aspects and to neglect others; topics which come into the latter category include reactions of species in their excited states, electron-transfer reactions involving metal complexes and the majority of the great body of reactions which have been studied using the stopped-flow technique (still the most widely used of the 'rapid reaction' techniques). There is certainly no wish to imply that these are less important than the topics which have been discussed, and it is likely that another author setting out to write a book of this type would have chosen somewhat differently. One of the attractive features of this field is the fact that the techniques involved are undergoing constant development and their application to new systems is continually revealing new information about chemical reactivity.

The primary aim in writing this book has been to bring some of this excitement to the attention of the more general chemist or biochemist. Any success which it might achieve in this direction is due in large measure to the stimulation received from teachers, colleagues and co-workers, but in particular from Professor Manfred Eigen, in whose laboratory it has been a great pleasure and privilege to spend several months. It goes without saying that these friends and colleagues are in no way responsible for the errors, omissions or other imperfections of the book.

DAVID N. HAGUE

Canterbury,
February, 1971

CONTENTS

CHAPTER 3 REACTIONS OF PROTONS, ELECTRONS AND METAL IONS

CHAPTER 4 RAPID REACTIONS IN BIOLOGICAL SYSTEMS

CHAPTER ONE

RAPID CHEMICAL REACTIONS

The quantitative study of chemistry has two aspects—static and kinetic Chemical kinetics dates from 1850 when Wilhelmy measured the rate of inversion of cane sugar, and its aims are generally twofold: to determine the macroscopic rate law of the overall reaction, together with the numerical value of the rate constant, and to analyse the mechanism of the reaction. Very few reactions are simple and before we can say that we understand a particular chemical reaction we must characterize its *elementary steps.* It is difficult to define an elementary step in absolute terms but a useful operational definition is that a reaction is an elementary step if it takes place in a simple irreducible act at molecular level. As our knowledge of molecular dynamics increases, so the number of steps in a reaction sequence which we regard as irreducible will also increase. One of the most powerful aspects of modern kinetics is the fact that it is possible to transfer the results of investigations of elementary reactions to more complicated situations, allowing us to predict the overall kinetic behaviour for a sequence of elementary steps.

Much of the classical theory of kinetics was developed for gas-phase reactions, where it is easy to see how this separation of a reaction into physically distinct steps can be valid. A classic example involves the reaction between hydrogen and bromine, which is stoichiometrically very simple: $H_2 + Br_2 = 2HBr$. Bodenstein showed that the rate law describing the formation of HBr is

$$\frac{\mathrm{d}[\mathrm{HBr}]}{\mathrm{d}t} = \frac{k[\mathrm{H_2}][\mathrm{Br_2}]^{\frac{1}{2}}}{k' + [\mathrm{HBr}]/[\mathrm{Br_2}]}$$

(where k and k' are composite rate constants) and proposed a mechanism in which the following steps are important:

(i) $Br_2 \rightleftharpoons 2Br$

(ii) $Br + H_2 \rightleftharpoons HBr + H$

(iii) $H + Br_2 \rightarrow HBr + Br$

In this case, the complicated nature of the overall rate law makes it comparatively easy to exclude many of the theoretically possible mechanisms.

The analogous reaction involving iodine illustrates the well-known fact that it is very difficult to claim that a mechanism is definitely the right one on the basis of kinetic studies alone, although it is often possible positively to exclude certain mechanisms. For many years the reaction $H_2 + I_2 \rightarrow 2HI$ has been quoted as the typical bimolecular gas reaction, involving the four-centre species (I), but Sullivan[1] has recently shown that very little, if any,

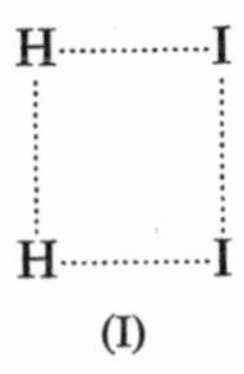

(I)

of the HI is made in a single step by the collision of H_2 and I_2 molecules. By comparing the rates of photochemical and thermal production of HI from hydrogen–iodine mixtures, he was able to show that the latter rate is consistent with two parallel series of elementary steps involving atoms, namely,

$$I_2 \rightleftharpoons 2I$$

$$H_2 + 2I \rightarrow 2HI$$

and,

$$I_2 \rightleftharpoons 2I$$

$$I + H_2 \rightleftharpoons HI + H$$

$$H + I_2 \rightleftharpoons HI + I$$

Perhaps further work will reveal some factor which will rule out one, or even both, of these pathways, but until then we are justified only in claiming that the data are *consistent* with this mechanism.

The long-term aim of kinetics is to predict the rates of reaction between any pair of species under any specified conditions, and also the nature of the products. Such predictions would use quantum mechanical descriptions of the species and involve construction of potential energy surfaces for the reaction, but we are a long way from being able to do this. However, one of the most exciting developments in gas-phase kinetics in recent years has been in the use of crossed molecular beams, which has provided a direct method for checking theoretical predictions experimentally at the molecular level. We discuss the method in greater detail in the next section. These studies are in their infancy, but there is no doubt that the method will be used much in the future as the theoretical side of reaction kinetics becomes better developed.

It is not possible to describe solution reactions in the same degree of detail because of the complications introduced by the solvent. Besides acting as a 'sink' for the removal of thermal energy released by the reaction, the solvent produces a 'cage' around the reactants which has two effects. On the one hand it becomes more difficult for two particular reactant molecules to meet but, once they have met, the 'cage' around the pair hinders their separation. It is generally estimated that the overall number of collisions is about the same in the gas phase and in solution, a reduction of about 10–100 in the number of encounters being balanced by a corresponding increase in the number of collisions per encounter. Despite the extra complications introduced by the 'cage' effect, it is still useful to discuss solution reactions in terms of their elementary steps. Thus an enzymic process consists of a sequence of steps such as complex formation, conformational change, proton transfer and complex dissociation, and it is possible to transfer the conclusions from the simple situation to the more complex one. Curiously, the 'cage' effect can result in some simplification of the theoretical problems in discussing the rates of reactions which are not diffusion-controlled. Because any given pair of molecules remain nearest neighbours for a relatively long time, we can replace the single-collision model by one in which there has been a quasi-equilibration of energy between the molecular pair and the environment.

We are particularly interested in these elementary steps because the majority of them are 'instantaneous'. The upper time limit on an instantaneous reaction will be taken as a few seconds. This is a rather arbitrary boundary but it approximates to the time which we can resolve with classical kinetic methods. The absolute lower time limit is imposed by the physics of molecular motion, and is the time taken for a bond to vibrate; if the bond is of the order of an Ångström unit, this implies a time of about 10^{-13} sec. For most practical purposes, however, the limit is imposed for solution reactions by the diffusion process. Thus either two reactants must come together or two products must separate (or both), and this typically takes a time of the order of 10^{-11}–10^{-10} sec. We are therefore interested in a time range spanning about twelve orders of magnitude, compared with the five or six orders covered by the classical range, and it is the range in which the majority of chemical reactions occur. In the last twenty or so years methods have been developed[2] for studying these very rapid reactions quantitatively. Many of them use principles which are rather different from those used in classical kinetics, and we shall discuss both the methods themselves (Chapter 2) and also some of the results which have been obtained using them (Chapters 3 and 4). A table showing typical rate constants which can be measured by the various methods is given in Appendix A.

Is it possible to make any generalizations about the type of chemical reaction which is likely to be very rapid? It is rather difficult to describe it in terms of a minimum rate constant or a maximum activation energy because of the effect of concentration on most reaction rates. Instead, it is convenient to use the operational definition that a reaction is instantaneous if it is too fast to follow by, for example, a vacuum-line system with pressure gauges for a gas reaction, or a pipette and stopwatch for a solution reaction. For gas reactions this generally implies that one of the reactants is a free radical or atom, although there is an abundance of reactions involving species in excited (e.g. triplet) states. We shall not discuss these even though many of them are very interesting and important. For systems in solution, especially aqueous, our definition includes most reactions involving ions, such as proton-transfer and metal-complex formation. It also includes most reactions of biological significance, such as enzyme processes and DNA replication.

It has been possible in the past to study some of these reactions with the help of simpler techniques. For example, reactions of order higher than one can be slowed down considerably by using very low concentrations of one or more reactant. This technique has been used very successfully by Bell and his school as a method of following acid–base reactions. The method is also widely used for studying reactions of enzymes and, indeed, much useful information has been obtained by the steady-state approach, including the observation that there is a remarkable similarity between the Michaelis–Menten rate law involving active sites on the enzyme and the Langmuir isotherm involving sites on the surface of a solid catalyst. The great disadvantage of this technique is that the extremely small concentrations of enzyme (often as low as 10^{-9} M) make it impossible to obtain kinetic information about any except the rate-determining process, which is one in a chain of many elementary steps. In particular cases it may be possible to change the rate-determining step by changing concentrations or substrate, but the conceptual difficulty is always there: we can only measure the overall process and this will only give *kinetic* information about the slowest step; steps prior to this show up as *equilibrium* constants and steps after this do not show up at all. If we can use stoichiometric quantities of the enzyme we can, in principle at least, obtain kinetic information about each of the elementary steps merely by looking at each in turn (there are severe practical difficulties over this, as we shall discuss further in Chapter 4, but at least it is possible in principle).

The other simple technique uses low temperature; as a working rule, many reactions are approximately doubled in rate for every 10° temperature rise and so if they are cooled sufficiently it is possible to slow them down to such an extent that classical methods can be used to study them.

This technique has not been used very widely, partly because of difficulties over freezing and partly because fast reactions tend to have low activation energies and hence the effect of temperature on their rates tends to be comparatively small.

The use of molecular beams

Molecular beams have been used in physical investigations for many years. A molecular beam differs from a gas jet in that the mean free path of the molecules in it is very much longer than the width of the beam. The consequence of this is that when a beam enters a region of low pressure it retains its identity whereas a jet disintegrates within a very short distance.

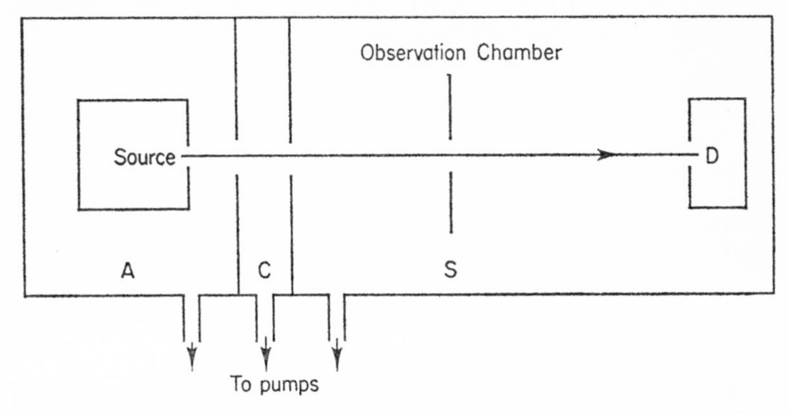

FIGURE 1.1 Schematic diagram of molecular-beam apparatus (see text).

A beam of a single chemical species, in which the molecules are moving effectively without collision, behaves in many ways like a beam of light. For example, it can be focused and will produce a well-defined shadow of an object placed in its path. In their classic experiment, Stern and Gerlach used an inhomogeneous magnetic field to split a beam of silver atoms and thereby experimentally confirmed the theoretical prediction of space quantization of angular momentum. In order to be able to follow a chemical reaction with molecular beams it is necessary to arrange for a beam of one reactant to interact with a beam of the other.

The details of a molecular beam apparatus depend to a large extent on the nature of the particular experiment, but Figure 1.1 shows how a single molecular beam may be produced. The molecules leave the source through a slit and enter the oven-chamber A, so-called because the beams used in many experiments are formed by evaporating a solid. The beam passes through a short isolating chamber C into the observation chamber, which contains a collimating slit S. The detecting device is at D. The restriction on the mean free path λ limits the width of the slits, which are typically of the order of 0·1 by 1·0 mm. It also limits the pressure P since λ is inversely proportional to P. The pressure is typically 10^{-6} torr or less. This is why the intensity of a molecular beam cannot be raised above what is really a very low level and one which requires a detector of extremely high sensitivity—if it were, λ would be reduced to such a level that the condition for effusive flow would not be met.

The detector is a critically important feature of any apparatus for following chemical reactions in crossed molecular beams. It frequently happens that no more than 10^4 molecules of product are arriving at the detector per second, and most of the normal techniques for measuring concentrations, such as spectrophotometry, are far too insensitive to detect them. The fact that the density of molecules in the beam is less by several powers of ten than the density of the residual gas in the apparatus increases the difficulties since the detector must evidently be able to distinguish between residual gas molecules and beam molecules.

Beams of alkali metal atoms M or molecules containing an alkali metal MX can be measured by a simple but highly efficient detector. The Langmuir–Taylor or surface-ionization detector makes use of the fact that M and MX lose electrons when they arrive at the surface of a suitable metal S:

$$M + S \rightarrow M^+ + e^- + S$$

$$MX + S \rightarrow M^+ + e^- + X + S$$

The reaction proceeds if the ionization potential of the alkali metal atom is less than the work function of the surface metal. The technique will only work, however, if a method can be found for distinguishing between free and bound M, thus enabling the detector to differentiate between elastically scattered atoms of the reactant beam and molecules MX produced by a reactive collision. Two parallel filaments of a platinum–tungsten alloy which have been pretreated in different ways allow such a discrimination. If the wire is heated in an oxygen atmosphere before use it will ionize both M and MX with an efficiency of almost 100%, but if it is preheated in methane it ionizes M with a high efficiency (~100%) but MX with a very low efficiency (~0·01%). The reason for this selective poisoning of the filament is not fully understood, but it allows the concentrations of M and MX to be determined at any position from the two positive ion currents. The surface-ionization detector is restricted to reactions involving the alkali metals and a few others but, in view of the power of the molecular-beam method, there is no doubt that ways will be found for extending these studies.

In the crossed beam apparatus (Figure 1.2) separate molecular beams containing the two reactant intersect in the centre and the angular distribution of the reaction products is determined by rotating the detector about the centre of the apparatus in (or close to) the plane of the two beams. One great advantage of the molecular-beam technique is that it is often possible to choose molecules with certain specified properties. For example, two rotating notched wheels can be used to reject those molecules

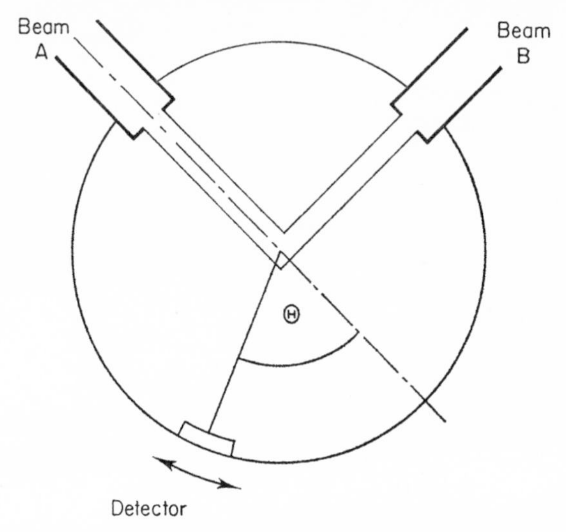

FIGURE 1.2 Schematic diagram of crossed molecular beam apparatus. Θ is the scattering angle for one species of product in laboratory coordinates.

moving with unwanted speeds, while electromagnetic fields can be used to align dipolar molecules. Since many of these selection methods work by rejecting unwanted molecules, the number of molecules in the beam, already very low, is considerably attenuated. Consequently, it is usual to select for different properties in turn.

What information is obtained in a typical molecular-beam experiment? In the collision theory of reaction rates the reaction cross-section is one of the functions which is required in order to be able to calculate *a priori* the rate constant for the reaction. The integral reaction cross-section and its dependence on energy can be determined by the molecular-beam method. (It is interesting to note that the introduction of the crossed molecular-beam technique has led to a renewed interest in the collision theory of reaction rates. Whereas rate data had been discussed almost exclusively in terms of the transition-state or absolute reaction rate theory, it is again becoming common to see discussions based on the collision theory.)

However, the angular distribution obtained from plots of product intensity against laboratory scattering angle Θ (Figure 1.2) are not suitable for direct interpretation in terms of collision dynamics. This is because the intensity at a given Θ depends also on the incident beam velocities (and hence the momenta of the reacting particles) and the angle of intersection of the two beams, so in the majority of experiments, where these properties

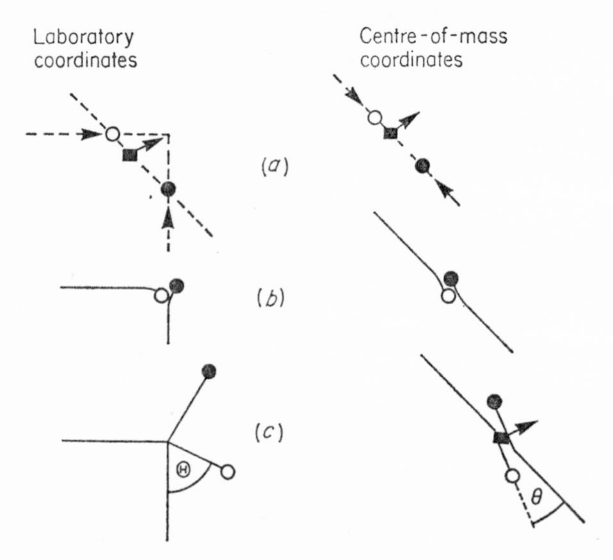

FIGURE 1.3 Schematic diagram representing the collision between a molecule of beam A (●) and one of beam B (○) in laboratory and centre-of-mass coordinates. (The centre-of-mass, which is represented by ■, has been omitted from (*b*) and (*c*, lab.) for clarity.) θ is the centre-of-mass scattering angle and Θ the laboratory scattering angle.

may not be unique, a given value of Θ is associated with a variety of different relative velocities. This difficulty can be overcome by describing the collision with respect to a moving coordinate system which does not change with respect to the apparatus parameters—namely, the centre-of-mass coordinate system.

Figure 1.3 illustrates the way in which a collision between two particles approaching each other at 90° in laboratory coordinates can be represented in *centre-of-mass coordinates*. Before the collision (*a*) the two particles are moving head-on towards each other along the direction of relative velocity $\mathbf{v}$ in the centre-of-mass system (i.e. an imaginary observer at the centre-of-mass sees one particle approaching from his left and the other particle from his right). After the collision (*c*) the particles separate with a new direction of relative velocity at an angle θ with respect to the direction of the incident relative velocity **v** ($\equiv \mathbf{v}_1 - \mathbf{v}_2$, the difference in absolute velocities of the two reacting particles). The transformation between coordinate systems can be performed by means of a 'Newton diagram', which makes use of the fact that momentum is conserved during the collision. The method is beyond the scope of this book but both it[3] and the way in which the integral reaction cross-section may be calculated[4] have been discussed elsewhere. We shall now discuss three types of reaction involving the alkali metals in which the distribution of the products appears to depend primarily on the type of reaction concerned.

In reactions of Type I the other reactant is a molecule in which a partially ionic bond is broken and the product is a molecule in which the new bond is more strongly ionic, for example, the reaction between K and CH_3I:

$$K + CH_3I \rightarrow KI + CH_3$$

The measured angular distribution of KI is shown in Figure 1.4(*a*), in which the maximum intensity is observed at a laboratory angle of 80° with respect to the incident K beam. This is shown in centre-of-mass coordinates

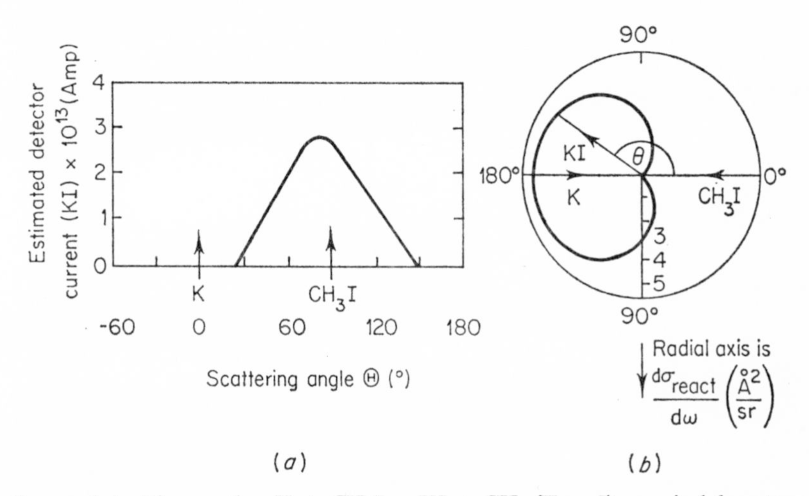

FIGURE 1.4 The reaction $K + CH_3I \rightarrow KI + CH_3$ (Type I) seen in laboratory (*a*) and centre-of-mass (*b*) coordinates (see text). [Data quoted in Ref. 4.]

in Figure 1.4(*b*), in which the differential cross-section ($d\sigma_{react}/d\omega$) is plotted in polar form as the radius against the centre-of-mass scattering angle θ. It will be seen that most of the products appear in the backward hemisphere with respect to the incoming potassium atom, and for this reason this is often called the 'rebound' mechanism. The anisotropic distribution suggests that the incident particles 'remember' their initial direction of approach, and hence the reaction time must be short compared with the time of rotation of the reactant atoms while they are together (i.e. the reaction time must be less than about 10^{-12} sec).

An interesting feature of molecular beam investigations is that it is possible to obtain a direct measure of the so-called steric factor. An unsatisfactory aspect of the collision theory of reaction rates had always been the fact that discrepancies between observed and calculated rate constants could usually be ascribed to the steric factor which could not, however, be measured directly. The steric factor in the case of Type I reactions is considerably less than unity: for K + CH_3I, there is a high probability of reaction whenever a potassium atom hits the I end of the methyl iodide molecule; when it hits the other end the probability of reaction would only be high if the reaction time were comparable with the time of rotation of the molecule—which it is not.

In reactions of Type II a purely covalent bond is replaced by one which is largely ionic—e.g.

$$K + Br_2 \rightarrow KBr + Br$$

Figure 1.5 shows that the maximum product intensities are found in the forward direction relative to the K beam, although the reaction cross-section for backward scattering is roughly the same as for the Type I

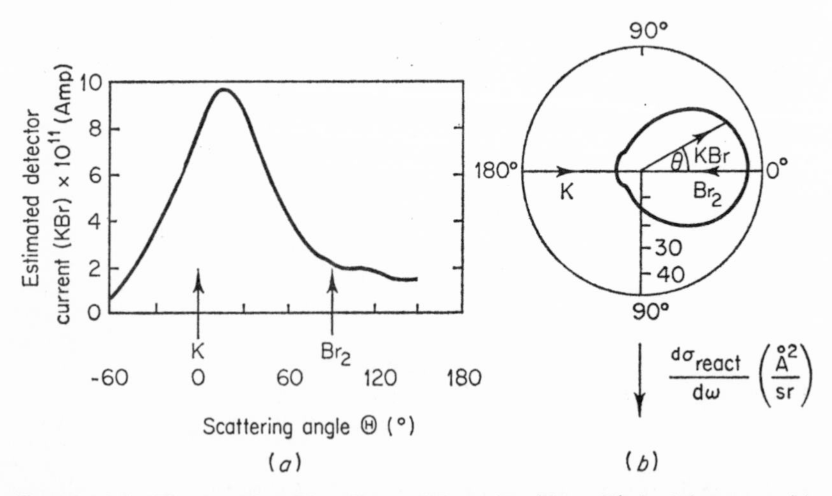

FIGURE 1.5 The reaction $K + Br_2 \rightarrow KBr + Br$ (Type II) in laboratory (*a*) and centre-of-mass (*b*) coordinates (see text). [Data quoted in Ref. 4.]

reactions. Thus the rebound mechanism holds for small impact parameters, but another mechanism is also important. The large peak in the forward direction is produced by the 'harpooning' mechanism in which the halogen molecule is 'harpooned' by an electron from the alkali metal atom. This can occur at large internuclear separation, so the reaction has a large cross-section. For the same reason as in Type I reactions it can be concluded that the reaction time is less than about 10^{-12} sec.

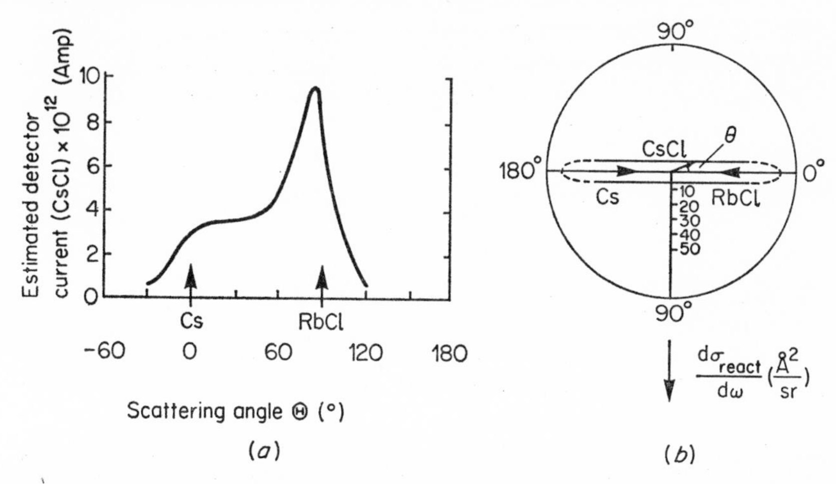

FIGURE 1.6 The reaction Cs + RbCl → CsCl + Rb (Type III) in laboratory (*a*) and centre-of-mass (*b*) coordinates (see text). [Data from W. B. Miller, S. A. Safron and D. R. Herschbach, *Disc. Faraday Soc.*, **44,** 108 (1967).]

Reactions of Type III involve the exchange of a group between two alkali metal atoms. Reactants and products are both ionically bonded, e.g.

$$Cs + RbCl \rightarrow CsCl + Rb$$

The rather different product distribution (Figure 1.6) has been explained in terms of the formation of a long-lived intermediate. The shape of the centre-of-mass distribution (Figure 1.6(*b*)) can be explained in terms of the conservation of angular momentum during the collision. The orbital angular momentum for large impact parameters is considerably larger than the rotational angular momentum of the RbCl, and if the lifetime of the intermediate is sufficiently long, then the total angular momentum is converted into rotational angular momentum. Because of the geometry of the triatomic intermediate, the chances of its decomposing in the forward or backward direction (relative to the direction of $\mathbf{v}$) are greater than in any other direction. It has been estimated that the lifetime of the intermediate must be greater than 5×10^{-12} sec.

The measurement of reaction cross-sections is bound to give a clearer understanding of the factors which govern chemical reactivity on a molecular scale, although the most serious lack at present is a manageable, i.e.

numerically and analytically soluble, theory of the potential energy hypersurfaces that govern a particular chemical reaction. The overall rate constant k, which is an average over many states, can readily be calculated from the reaction cross-section.

In contrast to the situation in the gas phase, the concept of reaction cross-section is not very well defined in solutions and it will probably be a long time before such detailed information as we have been considering will become available for reactions in the liquid phase. However, the recent developments in solution kinetics are no less exciting, and before discussing them in greater detail we shall consider briefly the theory of diffusion-controlled reactions since this allows us to estimate the maximum rate to be expected for a chemical reaction in solution.

Diffusion-controlled reactions

The theoretical treatments of this problem may be divided into two categories[5] (see Appendix B), one of which involves a consideration of the concentration gradients in the system while the other involves an analysis of the behaviour of a pair of diffusing molecules. The latter approach, which has been developed principally by Noyes, uses the probability of an encounter between two molecules derived from the random-walk theory. The other approach originated in the work of Smoluchowski, who applied Fick's laws of diffusion to the problem of the rate of coagulation of colloidal particles in solution.

Smoluchowski calculated[6] the number of times per second a given particle suspended in a liquid would be hit by one of the others as a result of their Brownian motion. If it is assumed that two reacting molecules, of which at least one is uncharged, can be likewise treated as spherical particles, it is possible to compute the number of times per second a molecule of type A collides with a molecule of type B. If the reaction is diffusion-controlled, this value is equal to the rate of the reaction.

Let us first consider the case of collision between two particles of the same type. One particle is considered to be fixed and the others diffuse from the bulk of the solution, in which the number of molecules per millilitre is n, into a hole surrounding it (at the boundary of the hole the concentration is taken as zero since any particles there would already have reacted). The particles are treated as spheres of diameter a (equal to the reaction distance), and in order to accommodate the Brownian motion of the fixed particle as well as that of all the others, the effective diffusion coefficient is taken as twice the normal diffusion coefficient D (or $D_A + D_B$ for a system involving particles of two types). The number of collisions per second ν is then given by $\nu = 8\pi Dan$. The Einstein equation for Brownian motion $D = \mathbf{k}T/\rho$ expresses the diffusion coefficient in terms of the frictional coefficient ρ of the sphere in the liquid, the Boltzmann constant $\mathbf{k}$ and absolute temperature T, and Stokes' law allows ρ to be determined from the viscosity $\eta: \rho = 3\pi\eta a$. By combining these equations, the number of collisions per second can be expressed as $\nu = (8\mathbf{k}T/3\eta)n$, giving a second order diffusion-controlled rate constant k_{DC} of $8RT/3000\eta$ l/mole sec.

It is interesting to note that the number of collisions per second is independent of the size of the particles. This is only strictly true for collisions between spherical particles of the same size. If the two particles are of different radii (r_A and r_B), then the Smoluchowski treatment leads to equation (1.1) for the diffusion-controlled rate constant.

$$k_{DC} = \left(\frac{2RT}{3000\eta}\right)\left(2 + \frac{r_A}{r_B} + \frac{r_B}{r_A}\right) \text{ l/mole sec} \quad (1.1)$$

Note that the influence of particle size is not very large. For example, if $r_A/r_B = 3$, the second bracket in equation (1.1) is $5\frac{1}{3}$ compared with 4 for $r_A = r_B$.

If the two reactants are both ions, equation (1.1) must be modified to take account of the interionic forces. Debye has[7] developed Smoluchowski's treatment to do this and has shown that equation (1.1) for k_{DC} is modified by a factor f. If the solution is very dilute, then the only extra force is the Coulomb force between the charged particles and

$$f = \delta/(e^{\delta} - 1)$$

where

$$\delta = \left(\frac{z_A z_B e^2}{\varepsilon \mathbf{k} T a}\right)$$

ε is the dielectric constant of the solvent, z_A and z_B are the charges on the ions and e is the electronic charge. However, if the solution is not very dilute account must also be taken of the screening effect of the counter-ion atmospheres around the reacting particles and the correction factor for equation (1.1) becomes $f' = f(1 + l/\lambda)$, where l is the equilibrium distance $z_A z_B e^2/(\varepsilon \mathbf{k} T)$ and the thickness of the ionic layer is

$$\lambda = \left(\frac{\varepsilon \mathbf{k} T}{8\pi e^2 I}\right)^{\frac{1}{2}}$$

where I is the ionic strength. The correction factors f, f' are greater than unity for unlike charges and less than unity for like charges.

The numerical value of k_{DC} for non-charged reactants calculated from equation (1.1) is approximately $0{\cdot}7 \times 10^{10}$ l/mole sec in water at 25°, with similar values in chloroform ($0{\cdot}95 \times 10^{10}$) and benzene ($1{\cdot}05 \times 10^{10}$).

For reactions between oppositely charged ions k_{DC} is increased by a factor up to about 10 (depending on a) to approximately 10^{11} l/mole sec in water. As is to be expected from equation (1.1), the rate constant of a diffusion-controlled reaction is inversely proportional to solvent viscosity and the activation energy is comparable to the activation energy of self-diffusion in the solvent (for water this is approximately 3·5 kcal/mole). A similar expression to (1.1) has been obtained for the diffusion-controlled value of a first order rate constant.[8]

In view of the simplifications used to evaluate them, the expressions for the diffusion-controlled rate constants can be no more than approximations. Thus, for example, no direct account has been taken of the solvent structure and such factors as the 'cage' effect. In spite of this, the relations provide a very useful basis for the discussion of instantaneous reactions in solution and they show that the important theoretical distinction should be made *not* between 'fast' and 'slow' reactions, but rather between diffusion- (i.e. physically) controlled reactions with second-order rate constants around 10^9–10^{11} l/mole sec, depending on the nature of the reactants and non-diffusion- (i.e. chemically) controlled reactions with second-order rate constants less than about 10^9 l/mole sec. In fact, fast non-diffusion-controlled reactions with rate constants less than about 10^7 l/mole sec provide the ideal subjects for the further development of chemical kinetics in solution; their great advantage is that they can be investigated, using many of the techniques described in the next chapter, in a fraction of the time required for a similar investigation of any of the 'classical' reactions.

REFERENCES

1. J. H. Sullivan, *J. Chem. Phys.*, **46,** 73 (1967).
2. *Z. Elektrochem.*, **64,** pp. 1–204 (1960); S. L. Friess, E. S. Lewis and A. Weissberger (Eds.), *Technique of Organic Chemistry*, Vol. 8, Part 2, *Investigation of Rates and Mechanisms of Reaction*, Interscience, New York, 1963; E. F. Caldin, *Fast Reactions in Solution*, Blackwell, Oxford, 1964; B. Chance, R. H. Eisenhardt, Q. H. Gibson and K. K. Lonberg-Holm (Eds.), *Rapid Mixing and Sampling Techniques in Biochemistry*, Academic Press, New York, 1964; K. Kustin (Ed.), *Methods in Enzymology*, Vol. 16, Academic Press, New York, 1969.
3. D. R. Herschbach, *Discussions Faraday Soc.*, **33,** 149 (1962).
4. J. P. Toennies, *Ber. Bunsenges. Physik. Chem.*, **72,** 927 (1968).
5. R. M. Noyes, in *Progress in Reaction Kinetics* (Ed. G. Porter), Vol. 1, Pergamon, Oxford, 1961, p. 129.
6. M. v. Smoluchowski, *Z. phys. Chem.*, **92,** 129 (1917).
7. P. Debye, *Trans. Electrochem. Soc.*, **82,** 265 (1942).
8. M. Eigen, W. Kruse, G. Maass and L. De Maeyer, in *Progress in Reaction Kinetics* (Ed. G. Porter), Vol. 2, Pergamon, London, 1964, p. 286.

CHAPTER TWO

EXPERIMENTAL METHODS

FLOW METHODS

Chronologically, the flow techniques were the first of the special methods for following fast reactions[1] to be developed, and even now they are possibly used more than all of the other techniques combined. The flow techniques may be seen as the logical extension of the classical 'mix and shake' method in which the reactants are now mixed within a fraction of a second. We shall discuss three variants which have been developed for

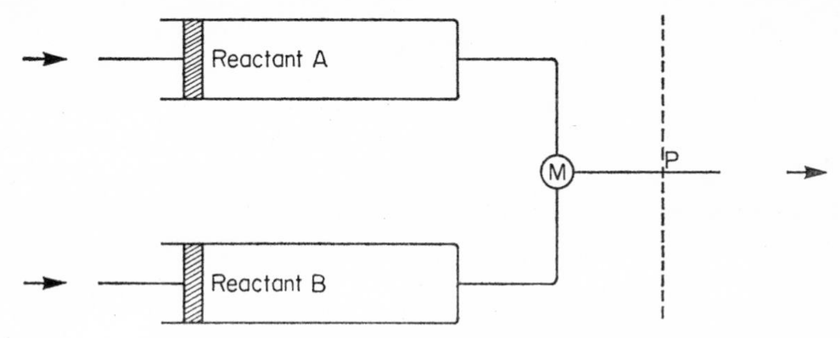

FIGURE 2.1 Schematic diagram of the flow–mix system, showing mixing chamber M and point of observation P.

following reactions in solution—stopped-flow, which is by far the most widely used, continuous-flow and accelerated-flow—and then consider the application of the method to reactions in the gas phase.

In the 1920's, Hartridge and Roughton at Cambridge were seeking a way of measuring the rate of reaction between oxygen and haemoglobin in water since they wanted to know whether this was the rate-determining step in the respiratory process. (Ironically, although they answered their original question the reaction between haemoglobin and gases is not yet completely characterized and is still a centre of controversy.) They passed the two reactant solutions from large reservoirs held at a constant head along two capillary tubes arranged to form a T-piece mixer (M, Figure 2.1) and determined the concentration of one or more of the reactants at P. In the mixer originally used, eight jets were arranged tangentially around the outlet tube and experiments showed that mixing was complete within a millisecond at a distance of 3 mm from the mixer. A source of monochromatic light and a photomultiplier coupled to an oscilloscope might be used at P to measure the composition of the solution. If the rate at which the mixed liquid flows along the outlet tube is v cm/sec and the distance from the mixer M to the observation point is x cm, the extent of the reaction in a small section of the reaction mixture corresponding to a known time x/v sec after the start of the reaction can be determined. In this, the *continuous-flow* method, the reaction profile is constructed by varying the flow rate (stepwise) and the distance x. Typically, v might be 5 m/sec and x 10 cm; the concentrations at P would therefore be those appropriate for 20 msec after the start of the reaction.

The great disadvantage of the continuous-flow method is the requirement of vast amounts of reactant solution. This problem is especially relevant for reactions involving substances of biological origin in spite of the nature of the original problem for which the technique was used; it would be out of the question to study reactions of most enzymes this way. Two main modifications have been introduced to overcome it, in both of which the distance x is now fixed at the minimum practical value, usually one or two centimetres. In the *accelerated-flow* method of Chance the reactants are driven from syringes and the concentration changes at P are followed from the start of the drive until the maximum flow-velocity has been achieved. The motion of the syringe driver-bar is also followed electronically. The conventional concentration–time reaction profile is constructed by making use of the fact that the time between mixing and observation is inversely proportional to the flow rate. Although the accelerated-flow method requires only small volumes of solution, the rather complicated electronic circuitry required has led to its eclipse by the stopped-flow method.

For the *stopped-flow* technique also the reagents are kept in two hypodermic syringes of equal volume, typically between 2 and 50 ml, and the plungers are pushed together so as to deliver equal amounts of the two solutions to the mixer. The syringes are mounted on a block and a bar, running on parallel guide-rods and pushed either manually or mechanically, ensures the even delivery of the solution (Figure 2.2). The reactant liquids are made to flow and are then stopped suddenly. This is done by passing the mixed solution into a third syringe arranged so that the plunger is forced against a stop and at the same time operates a microswitch. The latter disengages the drive motor and triggers a recording device at P, where the change in concentration of a small column of the mixed liquid is followed with time. By the time the mixed liquid has reached P a certain fraction of the reaction will be over. If the arrest of the liquid flow occurred instantaneously, which it obviously cannot, the half-life of the fastest observable reaction would be about x/v sec. The reaction half-life limit measurable by flow techniques is a few tenths of a millisecond at one end; at the other it is *n* seconds or even minutes, and is often determined by the diffusion of unreacted solution from the delivery tubes towards the observation position. With a stopped-flow apparatus it is possible to follow a complete reaction with only a fraction of a millilitre of each reagent—an ideal situation for enzyme reactions, cf. Chapter 4.

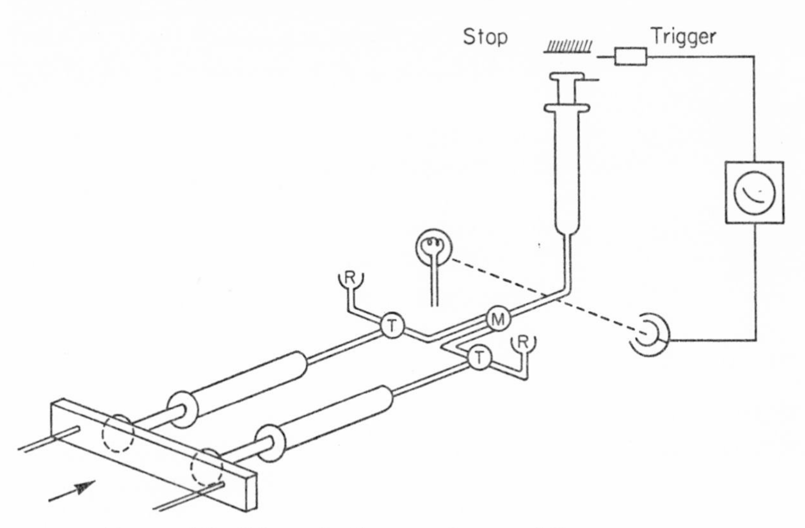

FIGURE 2.2 Schematic diagram of stopped-flow apparatus.

In a modification of the continuous-flow method, where each experiment yields only one point on the reaction profile plot, the reaction is quenched and analysed chemical or physically at leisure. Thus the reagents are mixed as usual and then at P they are mixed further with a substance which quenches the main reaction and a sample is removed for analysis. A reaction which has been studied[2] in this way is the radiochloride exchange in acetone of organosilicon chlorides with $*Cl^-$. The reaction was quenched by precipitating the free chloride ions as NaCl:

$$R_3SiCl + {*Cl^-} \rightleftharpoons R_3Si{*Cl} + Cl^-$$

followed by

$$Na^+ + \begin{cases} Cl^- \\ *Cl^- \end{cases} \rightarrow \begin{cases} NaCl \\ Na{*Cl} \end{cases}$$

The fraction of radiochloride was determined by counting the washed precipitate. In such a study the variables are v and x. The quenching technique has also been applied to reactions of biological importance.[3]

One of the inorganic systems which have been studied by flow methods[4] makes use of the fact that reactions with half-lives in the millisecond region may be followed, but faster reactions appear only as a shift in the baseline. The conventional stopped-flow technique was used and one reactant solution contained an organic halide RX and a cobalt(II) solution while the other contained sodium cyanide and an equivalent amount of NaOH to suppress hydrolysis. The reaction to be followed was that between the unstable $Co(CN)_5^{3-}$ species and the organic halide, but the former was prepared *in situ* since the first reaction is complete within the mixing time of the apparatus:

$$5CN^- + Co^{2+} = Co(CN)_5^{3-}$$

(very fast; occurs within the mixing time)

$$2Co(CN)_5^{3-} + RX = Co(CN)_5R^{3-} + Co(CN)_5X^{3-}$$

(fast; reaction followed at P).

The rate of the second reaction was followed by observing the increase in light absorbance at P due to the product $Co(CN)_5X^{3-}$ or the decrease in light absorbance due to the reactant $Co(CN)_5^{3-}$. (This illustrates very nicely the general aim in any kinetic study to observe both the formation of the products and the disappearance of the reactants. If the two rates coincide we can be fairly confident that the reaction is what we think it is.) A two-step mechanism was proposed for this reaction—the rate-determining production of R• radicals,

$$Co(CN)_5^{3-} + RX \rightarrow Co(CN)_5X^{3-} + R\bullet$$

being followed by their removal,

$$Co(CN)^{-3}_{5} + R\bullet \rightarrow Co(CN)_5R^{3-}$$

Flow methods have also been used for following reactions in the gas phase. One of the difficulties inherent in the study of fast gas reactions is that the absence of large concentrations of 'third bodies' means that the temperature equilibration tends to be comparatively slow. This is quite a serious problem in flow systems since it is difficult to counteract any thermal effects caused by the heat of reaction. In addition, any change in pressure associated with a mole number change and the pressure drop associated with the flow itself make it rather difficult to define the reaction conditions accurately. Despite this, the flow method has been used to determine the kinetics of many gas-phase reactions,[5] an inert diluent frequently being added.

The general experimental arrangement is similar to that shown in Figure 2.1. One reactant is passed along a tube inside a thermostatted compartment which is often, though not invariably, held at a comparatively high temperature. The other component is injected into the main stream and as the gases emerge from the thermostat they pass a detector, whose distance from the injection point may be varied. For each measurement the steady state is set up. The uncertainties in defining the reaction time and temperature are minimized by using long reaction tubes and low flow rates. It frequently happens that one of the reactants is in the atomic state. The atoms are made from the molecular species by passing it through a tube across which a radiofrequency discharge is applied between two external electrodes.

A reaction which has been studied by the flow method is the decay of nitrogen atoms in the presence of oxygen molecules,[6] $N + O_2 \rightarrow NO + O$. A stream of N atoms was generated from gaseous molecular nitrogen by passage through a discharge tube to which was coupled radiofrequency power. The stream was passed along a quartz reaction tube of about 150 cm length and 2 cm diameter held in a furnace at 150°–450°C. There were four inlet jets for admitting gas to the reaction system and they were approximately equally spaced along the reaction tube inside the furnace. The oxygen was admitted to the atomic N stream through the first jet and then at successive downstream jets nitric oxide was added. The latter was to determine the concentration of N atoms in the gas arriving at the particular jet since active nitrogen can be titrated with NO. The end-point is a sharp transition from a blue NO-emission to a yellow-green continuum, the 'air afterglow', which is associated with the combination of oxygen atoms and NO to give electronically excited NO_2 molecules. The end-point corresponds to the complete removal of N atoms by the very rapid reaction $N + NO \rightarrow N_2 + O$. The primary reaction was found to be first order in both N and O_2 and the second-order rate constant was $8{\cdot}3 \times 10^9 \exp(-7100/RT)$ l/mole sec.

For the kinetics investigation of fast reactions it is necessary to overcome two problems. In the first place the reaction has to be initiated and in the second its time course has to be observed. In flow techniques the classical principle of initiating a reaction by mixing the reactants has been extended, probably to its effective limit. In the remaining techniques novel principles are used for the initiation of the reaction.

LARGE PERTURBATIONS

The principle used by the methods to be described in this section is to apply a large perturbation to a system, thereby generating one of the reactants, and to follow the disappearance of this reactive species. In all of the methods to be considered, flash photolysis, pulse radiolysis and shock tube, it is necessary to use some form of rapid-detection device.

Flash photolysis

Flash photolysis is one of the few methods for studying the kinetics of fast reactions which have been applied with equal success to reactions in the gas and liquid phases. It was originally developed by Norrish and Porter for following gas reactions[7] and was first used for solution reactions[8] in 1954; it is applicable to reactions which are initiated by light. The reactants are subjected to a light flash of very high intensity in a region of the spectrum where at least one of the species is photosensitive. This species

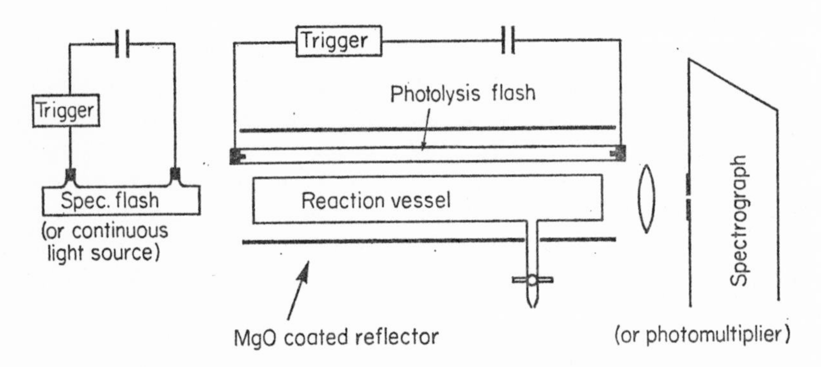

FIGURE 2.3 Typical flash-photolysis apparatus.

may dissociate into radicals or form triplets or some other excited state; and its fate is followed by means of subsequent light absorption or emission.

The exact form of apparatus used in a flash photolysis experiment depends to a large extent on the nature of the problem, but a typical one is shown in Figure 2.3. The reactants are placed in a cylindical quartz vessel 50 cm long and 2 cm in diameter which is mounted next to the photolytic flash tube. The latter is a quartz tube of about the same length as the reaction vessel which is filled with a rare gas, often krypton. The light emitted by the flash tube is a continuum extending over the whole of the visible range and well into the i.r. and u.v. on which are superimposed the broadened atomic spectral lines of the rare gas. The reaction vessel and flash lamp are mounted in a hollow cylinder whose inner surface is coated with magnesium oxide, which has a high reflectivity towards light of most wavelengths. A bank of condensers connected to the electrodes is charged up to the required voltage and then discharged by applying a triggering pulse to a small central electrode or to a spark gap in series with the flash tube. The duration time of the photolysis flash depends on the energy to be dissipated. The two conflicting demands of a short-lived but high-intensity burst have to be balanced, and the flash often has an energy of a few hundred joules spread over a few tens of microseconds.

When a new reaction is investigated it is usual to use a second light flash, the 'spectroscopic' flash, together with a spectrograph to follow the fate of the excited species. Another quartz flash tube, rather smaller than the photolysis lamp and with one of its ends transparent (the electrode may be built into the side of the tube) is mounted along the axis of the reaction vessel. At the other end of the vessel is the spectrograph with plate camera. The spectroscopic flash is triggered electronically with a photocell which picks up light from the photolysis flash and is timed to go off between 10^{-5} and 1 sec after the main flash. The absorption spectra of the reaction mixture before and at known times after photolysis are compared, and a suitable wavelength is chosen at which to study the reaction kinetically. The spectroscopic flash and spectrograph are then replaced by a high-intensity source of monochromatic light and a photomultiplier coupled to an oscilloscope. One of the advantages of the method is that, because of the comparatively large optical path-length, it is possible to detect species with low extinction coefficient or which are present in very small concentration.

One consequence of the large energies used in flash photolysis is that very large temperature rises might be involved—often as high as several hundreds of degrees. The temperature rise and its accompanying pressure rise may affect the rate constants directly; they may also interfere with the analysis by producing inhomogeneities in the reaction system. In solution reactions the heating is never significant since the solvent acts as a very efficient thermostat. The same result can often be achieved in gas reactions by the addition of large amounts of an inert gas.

It is sometimes difficult to identify a transient species from its spectrum alone. In certain cases it is possible to determine the spectrum of an intermediate on an absolute scale by making use of the changes in the spectrum of one of the reactants. The fraction of the reactant which is decomposed is readily measured, and it is assumed to have been completely converted into the intermediate. This gives a measure of the absolute concentration of the intermediate and so, if the optical density is measured, the extinction coefficient can be determined. This approach is especially useful if an excited molecular state, such as a triplet, is involved. Where this approach is not possible, a relative concentration scale can be established and from this the reaction half-lives measured. If, as often happens, the concentration of the intermediate changes much more rapidly than the temperature or pressure, then we can assume that if the same intensity is found with a given system at different times by using path-lengths in the ratio a:b, then the concentrations at these times are in the ratio b:a. This is a direct consequence of Beer's Law.

The flash technique we have described allows reactions down to the microsecond range to be studied but the finite time required to discharge the energy through the flash lamp means that times much shorter than this are unlikely to be achieved with such an apparatus. Porter has recently

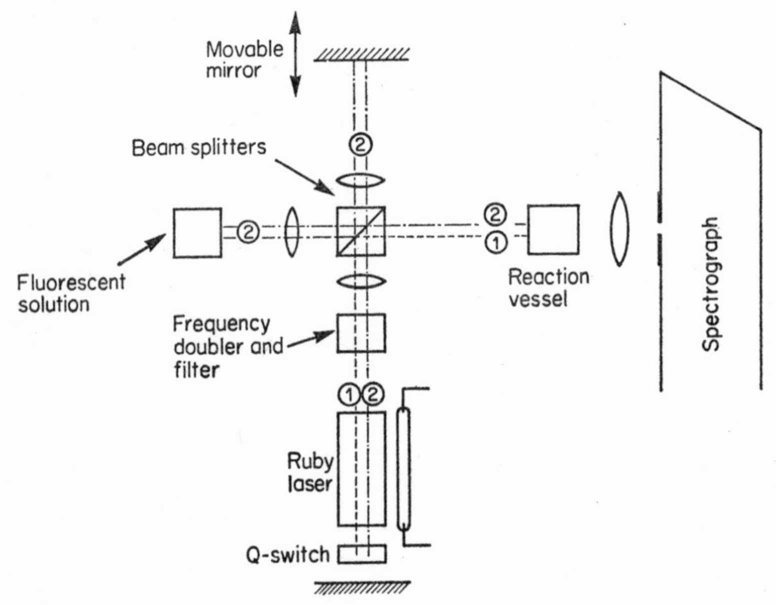

FIGURE 2.4 Nanosecond flash-photolysis apparatus.

described[9] a very elegant modification of the technique which uses a laser and allows reactions in the nanosecond range to be studied. The method has the advantage of simplicity and the principles involved make it capable of operating equally well in the sub-nanosecond range. A ruby laser fitted with a vanadyl phthalocyanine Q-switch* delivers a 70 mJ pulse of light lasting 18 nsec, which is frequency doubled to 347 nm by an ADPH (ammonium dihydrogen phosphate) crystal, filtered and then split (Figure 2.4). The first part of the split beam passes directly into the reaction vessel and acts as the photolysis flash. The second part acts eventually as the

* A Q-switch is a device for ensuring that the energy delivered by a laser is concentrated in a very short time. A flash light placed alongside the ruby rod provides the energy but, in order for the laser action to occur, one end of the rod must be totally internally reflecting and the other—through which the beam emerges—partially internally reflecting. A Q-switch makes one of the ends reflecting 'instantaneously' some time after the laser material has absorbed the excitation energy from the flash light, with the result that a large burst of light emerges from the laser within a few nanoseconds.

spectroscopic flash but it is delayed to a known extent by a rather ingenious method. It is reflected off a movable plane mirror which can be adjusted to give a delay of up to 100 nsec and then, via the beam splitter, into a cell containing a fluorescent solution (1,1′,4,4′-tetraphenyl buta 1,3-diene in cyclohexane). This solution emits a pulse of light which is continuous over the wavelength range 400–600 nm and which lasts as long as the laser pulse, namely 18 nsec. The spectroscopic pulse is then passed into the reaction vessel and thence to the slit of a spectrograph, in the normal way. It is possible to obtain accurately reproducible delays between the photolysis and spectroscopic flash in this way and the time resolution is limited only by the duration of the laser pulse. The nanosecond flash-photolysis technique is being used to observe excited singlet states which have lifetimes in this range and are often the precursors of the triplet states which are observed in the microsecond range.

As an example of a system which has been studied by flash photolysis we shall consider the elucidation of the role of lead tetra-ethyl (LTE) as an antiknock. The phenomenon of knock in the internal combustion engine is connected with high compression ratios and results in heavy loss of power and, in extreme cases, the destruction of the engine. Using high-speed photography it was shown in the late 1940's that knock is caused by detonation waves which originate in centres of auto-ignition in the highly compressed and heated combustion mixture. Empirically, the addition of a small amount of lead tetra-ethyl to the fuel was found to quench the knocking, but it was not known whether the lead compound acted homogeneously or heterogeneously, for example, in the form of a colloidal smoke of Pb or PbO or at the surface of the vessel. Erhard and Norrish[10] investigated the systems acetylene or hexane (suitable hydrocarbons which exhibit knock), oxygen and amyl nitrite in the absence and presence of LTE, using an apparatus which allowed them to detect intermediates by their emission as well as their absorption spectra. Amyl nitrite was used because it is known to be a strong pro-knock agent; it also acts as a sensitizer, absorbing light and thereby being split into radicals which initiate the reaction, and yet it is not so reactive as to decompose the LTE before photolysis. Let us consider first the system without LTE.

As for many hydrocarbons, the combustion of acetylene and hexane proceeds in two stages. An induction period, generally lasting for 20–150 μsec, following the immediate disappearance of the spectrum of amyl nitrite, is followed by the combustion proper. During the precombustion step no spectrum of a free radical can be detected and it is thought that among the products at this stage are such oxygen-rich species as aldehydes and peroxides. After this induction period the absorption spectra of diatomic radicals appear rapidly, reaching their maximum values at times which are always less than 200 μsec after initiation (Figure 2.5), and their subsequent decay extends over a period of several milliseconds. These radicals are primarily OH, but low concentrations of CN and NH can also be detected. The emission spectra of the radicals can also be picked up and a strikingly similar time variation is observed. The knocking could be seen clearly and corresponded to the peak concentration of the radicals. It was shown, incidentally, to be stronger in mixtures with shorter induction periods. Presumably the initiation is not completely homogeneous and a slight overheating of a small portion of the reaction mixture in the flash tube (see p. 21) results in detonation waves by promoting the ignition in that particular region—as in the internal combustion engine.

The addition of small amounts of LTE has two effects: the induction period is increased by several hundred per cent, the appearance of OH radicals being correspondingly delayed (Figure 2.5) and the incidence of detonation is greatly reduced or even eliminated. The dominant intermediate species present in this long induction period are Pb and PbO and they reduce the tendency to knocking in two ways. In the first place, atomic lead derived from the LTE by photolysis or pyrolysis reacts preferentially with the oxygenated compounds such as aldehydes and peroxides which act as centres of autoxidation in the precombustion stage. By reducing their concentrations the Pb interrupts the chain reactions of which they are a part. In the second place, the PbO formed in this reaction reacts with the hydrocarbon radicals involved in the chains, forming atomic lead. As the OH radicals begin to appear they, too, are removed by the Pb. Thus, by alternately being oxidized to PbO and then reduced back to Pb, the lead interrupts the chain reactions which normally lead to preignition. At the moment of ignition the PbO is dissociated by the heat of the flame and only the vapour of atomic lead remains.

Photosynthesis is another process which has been studied with the help of flash photolysis. The effect of light on the various components of chloroplasts has been followed, using both extracts and also the whole chloroplasts themselves. This topic, which is outside the scope of this book, has been reviewed recently by Witt.[11] Witt has used a technique known as *periodic flash photolysis* to extend considerably the sensitivity and time range which are obtainable. The conventional technique can measure transmission changes of 0·01% in times as short as 10^{-3} sec, but he makes use of the fact that, if a measurement can be made several times, its accuracy increases with the square root of the number of recordings. By storing many traces of the complete reaction in a computer of average transients (CAT) he has been able to measure optical density changes as small as 0·0001 at about 50 μsec after the flash. Another technique is to divide the complete reaction sequence into small time segments by using

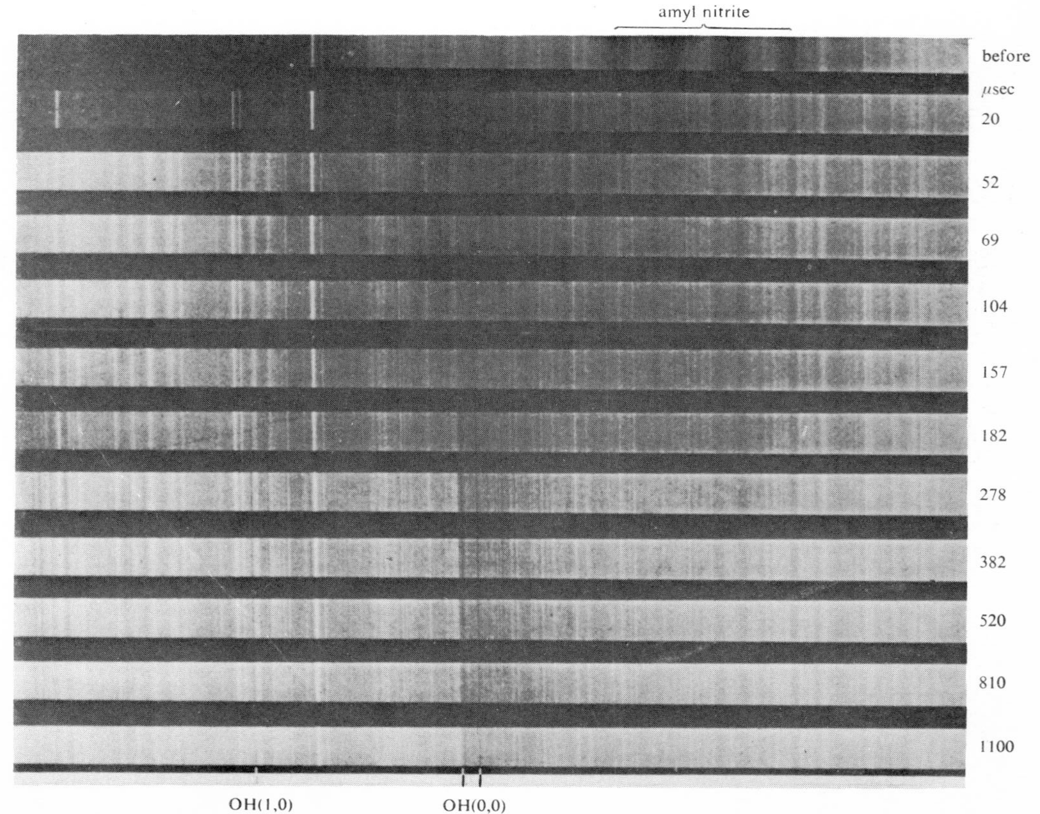

FIGURE 2.5 Spectra against time for the system amyl nitrite (4 mm), acetylene (3·3 mm) and oxygen (20 mm). (a) without LTE

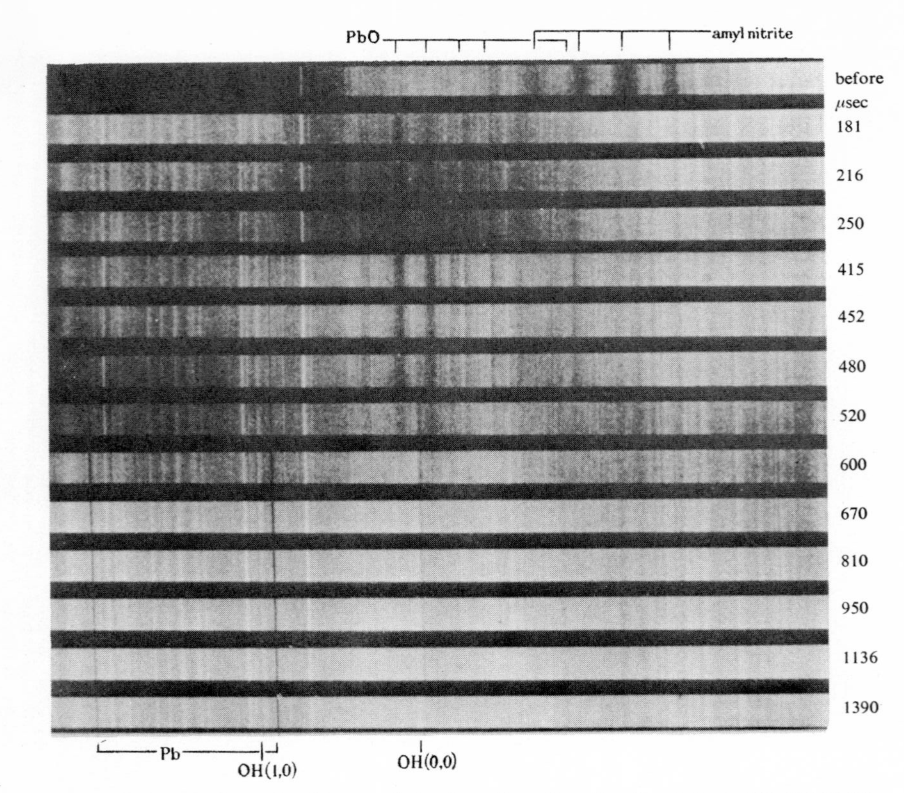

(b) with LTE (0·17 mm). Reproduced by permission from *Proc. Roy. Soc.* (*London*), *A.*, **234,** 178 (1956)

choppers in conjunction with the flashes and to measure the absorption of the system during a given segment many times. The absorption of the next segment is then measured, and so on, until the entire course of the reaction has been covered. Again, it is necessary to use a CAT.

Pulse radiolysis

Pulse radiolysis is in many ways a similar technique and may be regarded as the radiation equivalent of flash photolysis with a pulse of ionizing radiation replacing the photolytic light flash. It has been applied primarily to reactions in solution and has been used with great success for the investigation of reactions of the hydrated electron.

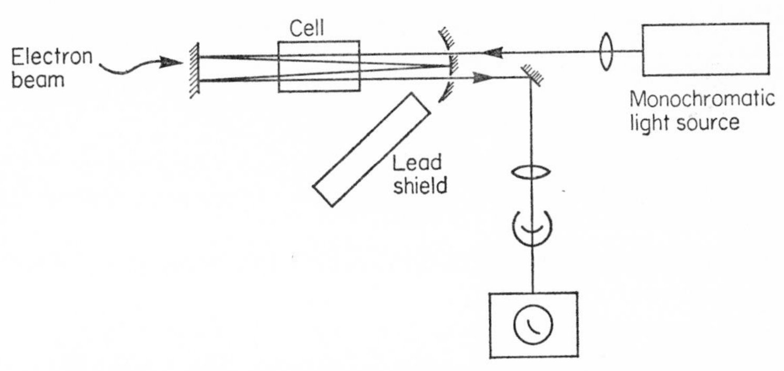

FIGURE 2.6 Schematic diagram of the pulse-radiolysis apparatus.

A typical pulse-radiolysis apparatus is shown in Figure 2.6. A pulse of electrons from a linear accelerator is passed through the solution and the changes produced are followed spectrophotometrically,[12] either at a known time after the electron pulse with a spectroscopic flash and a spectrograph, or continuously at a fixed wavelength with a steady light source and a photomultiplier. The same opposing demands of short duration and high intensity apply for the radiation pulse as for the principal flash in flash photolysis. Typically the pulse, which may be of X-rays rather than electrons, lasts for one or two microseconds. With this technique it is particularly important to remove the last traces of impurity from the solution since these frequently interfere with the reaction under investigation. This can be done in a particularly elegant way when reactions of the hydrated electron are being investigated. The aqueous electrons produced on irradiation are found to disappear more slowly (see p. 96) after successive pulses and it seems that they are reacting with the residual impurities to give non-reactive products. The solutions are therefore pulsed until the electron decays at a reproducible rate, by which time it is assumed that all of the reactive impurities have been removed. This generally happens after about twenty pulses.

Rather than discuss at this stage reactions which have been studied by pulse radiolysis we consider in Chapter 3 the kinetic properties of the hydrated electron, which have been determined to a large extent by this technique. The method has also been used to follow reactions of the secondary or tertiary products of the radiolysis. For example, if an aqueous solution of Fe^{2+} is radiolysed some of the oxidizing fragments of the water radiolysis, such as OH radicals, are capable of extracting an electron from the metal ion to produce Fe^{3+}. The subsequent complex formation of this ion with ligands in the solution, such as SO_4^{2-}, can then be followed. Evidently the scope for such applications is considerable, although the reactions are frequently so complex that it is not quite certain what is going on.

Shock tube

The third large-perturbation technique which we shall consider involves the *shock tube*. Although the method has been used to a limited extent with reactions in the condensed phase its prime kinetic application has been for very fast reactions in the gas phase.[13] The reactants are contained in a long narrow tube, the shock tube, and are subjected to a very sudden increase in pressure. This may be as large as 10^6 atmospheres and it may

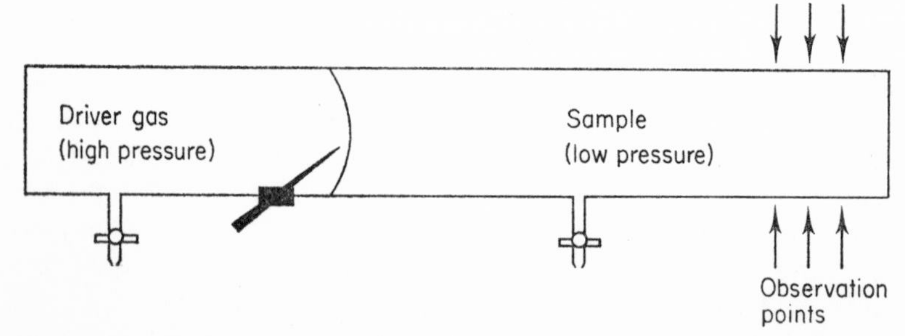

FIGURE 2.7 Schematic diagram of shock tube for use with gaseous systems.

occur within 10^{-9} sec and be associated with a temperature rise of as much as 10^7 °K, so the shock is sufficient to excite the molecules present and often to bring about their dissociation into radicals and atoms. The subsequent behaviour of these radicals is followed.

In principle, the design of the shock tube is very simple; it is illustrated in Figure 2.7. A smooth metal or glass tube about 20 ft long and a few inches in diameter is divided into two compartments by a thin diaphragm made of a suitable material such as cellophane or aluminium foil. About a third of the tube comprises a high-pressure region containing a 'driver' gas, often hydrogen or helium. The remainder of the tube is a comparatively low-pressure region containing the gas mixture, usually carried in 90% argon so that the density and temperature of the gas in the shock front are determined by the non-reacting carrier gas. The experiment is started by puncturing the diaphragm with a sharp needle. This produces

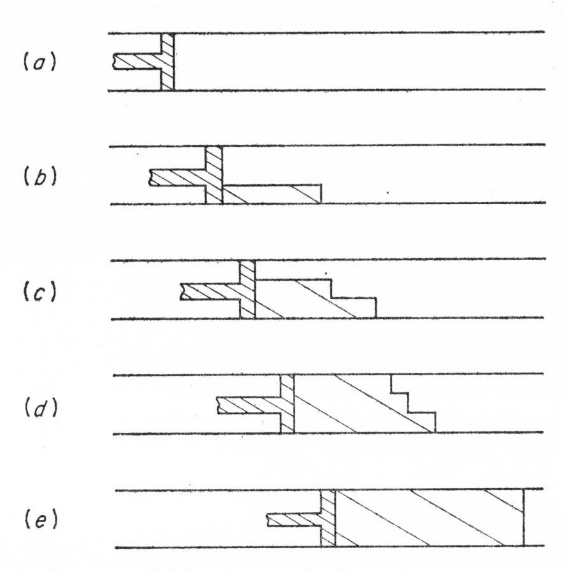

FIGURE 2.8 Becker's model for the production of a shock wave. [*Z. physik.*, **8**, 321 (1922).]

a shock wave which enters the low-pressure region and moves rapidly towards the end of the tube. Just before the end it passes several observation points located along the side of the tube.

How is this shock wave produced? A useful model for visualizing the formation of a shock was first proposed by Becker in 1922. He compares the high-pressure region with a tight-fitting piston in a tube. At the moment the diaphragm breaks the imaginary piston is instantaneously at rest but it rapidly accelerates into the low-pressure area. This acceleration is seen as a stepwise process (Figure 2.8) in which each displacement generates a pressure pulse which travels into the gas ahead. Each pulse raises the gas to the piston velocity and it also raises its temperature adiabatically. Because the speed of sound is higher at higher temperatures the second, third and subsequent pulses tend to catch up with the first. Eventually, the pulses all coalesce and form a large discontinuity which moves at constant speed along the tube. The term 'shock wave' is somewhat misleading since the pulse is actually a single sharp transition between two sets of essentially uniform conditions. The size of this transition zone is very small. It is difficult to measure it accurately, but there are indications that it is typically of the same order of magnitude as the wavelength of visible light, about 10^{-4} cm. The gas is therefore heated very rapidly within a few collision path-lengths, gaining a considerable amount of kinetic energy and entropy in a short time. Equations can be derived which relate the energy, pressure, density and temperature of the gas on entering and leaving the transition zone by using the two equations of state of the gas and expressions for the conservation of mass, energy and momentum. The functions of the observation points in Figure 2.7 are twofold. In the first place they are to measure the velocity of the shock. Although the shock wave involves a uniform slug of gas (i.e. there is essentially no temperature gradient perpendicular to the axis of the tube) the thin layer of gas immediately next to the wall is not heated to the same extent as that in the centre. The temperature rise at the wall cannot, therefore, be used as an indication of the temperature rise in the bulk of the gas, although it can be used as an indication of the passage of the shock front. The time taken for the shock wave to pass between sets of small platinum sensors deposited on plates fixed flush with the wall (whose electrical conductivity is temperature-dependent) is measured. The second function of the observation points is to pick up spectral changes associated with the production and subsequent reaction of free radicals and excited species. This, actually, is one of the greatest experimental difficulties with this technique because of the small spectral changes which take place on a very short time scale.

Associated with the production of the high-pressure shock front there is inevitably a low-pressure or 'rarefaction' wave produced concurrently at the diaphragm. This moves initially in the opposite direction from the shock wave but is reflected by the back wall of the tube, and so eventually follows the main shock wave down the tube. The rarefaction wave tends to catch up with the shock wave and, because of the simplifications it allows, it is often convenient to make the measurements on the shocked gas before it arrives, that is, within about 10^{-6} to 10^{-3} sec. However, it is also possible to use this low-pressure wave to quench the reactions which had been going on at the high temperature and then to remove the gases and analyse them by means of a mass spectrometer. By varying the relative pressures in the two regions of the tube it is possible to vary the time for which the reactant gas is at the high temperature and pressure.

As we have indicated, this method is useful for following gas reactions. It is particularly valuable for studying reactions in which wall effects interfere, such as explosions, since these can be avoided altogether. One reaction which has been studied in shock tubes is that between hydrogen and oxygen.[14] The course of the reaction is followed by measuring the absorption due to OH radicals. These are used because they have comparatively intense absorption lines and are relatively stable. Light is passed through two quartz windows set opposite each other into the side of the tube and is picked up by a photomultiplier. This light is particularly rich in OH spectral lines since it is produced by discharging a flashlamp containing water vapour. Reaction zone temperatures in the range 1150°–1850°K and pressures of a few atmospheres were achieved. By analysing the change in absorption by the OH radicals as a function of the time behind the shock front, it was possible to deduce the relative importance of the various reaction paths for the recombination of the radicals produced with different $H_2:O_2$ ratios.

We have suggested that shock tubes can also be applied to reactions in liquids. The comparative incompressibility of liquids compared with gases means that with the pressures readily obtainable in the laboratory (i.e. without the use of explosives) the temperature and pressure rises are comparatively small. In fact, a little work has been done with liquid systems[15] and the pressure rise of a few hundred atmospheres and temperature rise of a few degrees make this an ideal relaxation method (see section 3). Kinetics of proton-transfer reactions have been studied in this way (Chapter 3).

SMALL PERTURBATIONS: CHEMICAL RELAXATION METHODS

The chemical relaxation methods developed by Eigen[16] are based on another way of overcoming the problem of initiating the reaction in a time which is short compared with the limit imposed by physical mixing. We start with the system 'in equilibrium', give it a *small* disturbance by some physical means, and observe the way in which the new equilibrium is established. The difference from the methods described in the previous section is in the size of the perturbation, since with chemical relaxation methods there is no large-scale generation of reactants. The methods have been used only with reactions in solution. We shall discuss them in terms of the step-function, or transient techniques, partly because it is comparatively easy to visualize what is taking place and partly because one of them, the temperature-jump technique, is the chemical relaxation method which is most widely used.

Suppose we have the simple equilibrium represented by equation (2.1) and only species C absorbs light at a certain wavelength. If the equilibrium is suddenly displaced, we can illustrate the way in which the absorbance of

$$A + B \underset{k_{21}}{\overset{k_{12}}{\rightleftharpoons}} C \tag{2.1}$$

the solution changes as the new equilibrium position is established by Figure 2.9. The displacement is 'instantaneous' and occurs at time t_0; the difference in the absorbance due to the equilibrium concentrations of species C under the initial and final conditions is given by d_0.

We can imagine three ways in which the system can behave. If the reaction is very slow the old equilibrium position will be maintained and

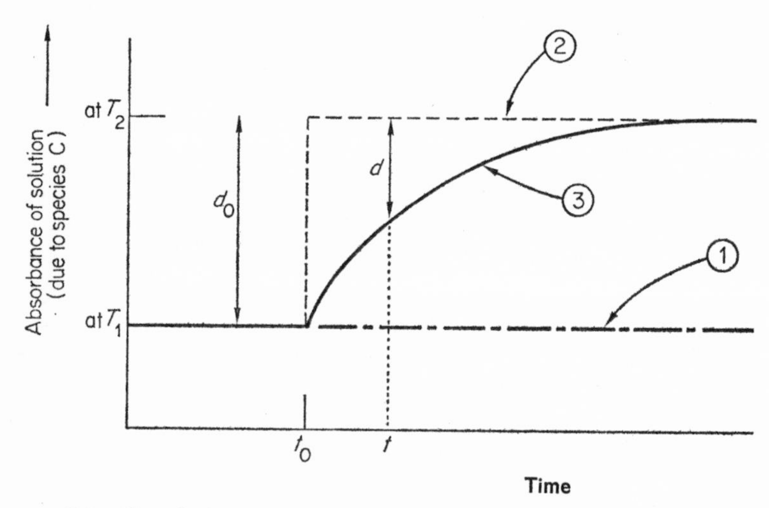

FIGURE 2.9 Chemical relaxation in terms of the step-function model. The disturbance of reaction (2.1) occurs at time t_0.

essentially no change in absorbance will be seen on the time scale of the experiment (curve 1); if the reaction is very fast, the new equilibrium will be set up in a very short time, i.e. the chemical system follows the physical disturbance very closely (curve 2); if the reaction responds at some intermediate rate, the chemical readjustment can be seen taking place (curve 3). If one very important condition is fulfilled, namely that the displacement is small (i.e. that the *change* in concentration is much less than the *absolute* concentration), then the reaction curve follows an exponential, irrespective of the kinetic order of the reaction. This exponential is described by the equation $d = d_0 \, e^{-t/\tau}$ where d is the difference in the absorbance between the new equilibrium value and that at time t, and τ is the *relaxation time* of the system. τ is the time taken for d to fall to $1/e$ of its original value, i.e. to approximately $\frac{3}{8}d_0$; it depends only on the particular chemical system under investigation and is independent of the method used to follow it. (Note that τ is comparable in size to the reaction half-life. The latter, $t_{\frac{1}{2}}$, would be the time taken for d to fall to $\frac{1}{2}d_0$.)

The term relaxation can be applied to many effects. For example, it was first used by Maxwell in connection with the viscosity of fluids and it has been used by Debye to describe the time taken for dipoles to orientate themselves in a changing magnetic field; we shall use it further in the section dealing with the application of n.m.r. to kinetics (pp. 48–66). The essential feature of all relaxation processes is that there is a recognizable delay between cause and effect. When the delay in response is caused by the finite time taken for two or more chemical components to react the process is called *chemical relaxation*. The way in which the system relaxes may be related to the rate constants for the reactions involved in the equilibrium, and before we consider the various relaxation techniques in greater detail we shall look at this relationship in a general way.[17]

Referring to reaction (2.1),

$$A + B \underset{k_{21}}{\overset{k_{12}}{\rightleftharpoons}} C \tag{2.1}$$

if we represent the (new) equilibrium concentrations of A, B and C by, respectively, $\bar{c}_A$, $\bar{c}_B$ and $\bar{c}_C$ and the deviations of the concentrations from these values at time t by $\Delta\bar{c}_A$, $\Delta\bar{c}_B$ and $\Delta\bar{c}_C$, then the actual concentrations at time t are $(\bar{c}_A - \Delta\bar{c}_A)$, $(\bar{c}_B - \Delta\bar{c}_B)$ and $(\bar{c}_C - \Delta\bar{c}_C)$. We can then write the ordinary kinetic equation for the rates of formation of A, B and C at time t. For example,

$$\frac{\mathrm{d}(\bar{c}_C - \Delta\bar{c}_C)}{\mathrm{d}t} = k_{12}(\bar{c}_A - \Delta\bar{c}_A)(\bar{c}_B - \Delta\bar{c}_B) - k_{21}(\bar{c}_C - \Delta\bar{c}_C)$$

i.e.

$$\frac{\mathrm{d}\bar{c}_C}{\mathrm{d}t} - \frac{\mathrm{d}\Delta\bar{c}_C}{\mathrm{d}t} = k_{12}\bar{c}_A\bar{c}_B - k_{21}\bar{c}_C - k_{12}(\Delta\bar{c}_A\bar{c}_B + \Delta\bar{c}_B\bar{c}_A) + k_{12}\Delta\bar{c}_A\Delta\bar{c}_B + k_{21}\Delta\bar{c}_C$$

We now use three other pieces of information:

(i) At the equilibrium position the $\Delta\bar{c}$ terms are zero, hence

$$\frac{\mathrm{d}\bar{c}_C}{\mathrm{d}t} = k_{12}\bar{c}_A\bar{c}_B - k_{21}\bar{c}_C (= 0)$$

(ii) Since the disturbance is small, $\Delta\bar{c}_A\Delta\bar{c}_B$ is negligible compared with $\Delta\bar{c}_A\bar{c}_B$ and $\Delta\bar{c}_B\bar{c}_A$.

(iii) From the stoichiometry of the system, $\Delta\bar{c}_C = -\Delta\bar{c}_A = -\Delta\bar{c}_B$. Therefore

$$\frac{-\mathrm{d}\Delta\bar{c}_C}{\mathrm{d}t} = k_{12}(\bar{c}_A + \bar{c}_B)\Delta\bar{c}_C + k_{21}\Delta\bar{c}_C$$

which is of the form $dx/dt = -kx$, i.e. it represents an exponential $x = x_0 e^{-kt}$ of which the constant term $k(\equiv\tau^{-1})$ is given by

$$[k_{12}(\bar{c}_A + \bar{c}_B) + k_{21}].$$

Thus, by investigating the variation of τ^{-1} with $(\bar{c}_A + \bar{c}_B)$, we can obtain k_{12} from the slope of the straight line plot and k_{21} from the intercept. Their ratio is equal to the equilibrium constant which can be measured independently by non-kinetic methods, thus providing an independent check on the mechanism. (Note that if condition (ii) above is not obeyed, the resulting curve will not necessarily be exponential. By using small perturbations we can employ the very convenient 'linearizing' procedure.)

The situation in chemical relaxation is rather similar to that in which a conventional technique is being used to follow the kinetics of a reaction which does not go to completion—in the sense that the apparent rate constant contains the *sum* of contributions from both the forward and backward steps. Use can be made of this fact when working out the expression for τ^{-1} for a particular mechanism since the overall τ^{-1} is merely the sum of the individual contributions for the two half-reactions (Table 2.1). For example, a system

$$A + B \underset{k_{21}}{\overset{k_{12}}{\rightleftharpoons}} C + D$$

in which B is buffered has a reciprocal relaxation time given by

$$\tau^{-1} = k_{12}\bar{c}_B + k_{21}(\bar{c}_C + \bar{c}_D)$$

Note that if species B is buffered or quasibuffered (present in large excess) its concentration does not change during the reaction. Hence $\Delta\bar{c}_B = 0$, with the result that the concentration term(s) multiplying $\Delta\bar{c}_B$ in the rate equation do not appear in the final expression, and the contribution to τ^{-1} provided by the forward reaction is $k_{12}\bar{c}_B$. Often, the individual rate constants can be determined from kinetic measurements alone by a plot of τ^{-1} against a suitable concentration function, but for a reaction which is first order in both directions it is necessary to measure the equilibrium constant in order to separate k_{12} and k_{21} (since $\tau^{-1} = k_{12} + k_{21}$).

So far we have only considered reactions which involve a single step. One of the powerful features of the relaxation technique is that it may be extended to cover reactions which have several consecutive steps, so that a reaction may be split up into its elementary steps.

If the transformation between two states, e.g. $A \rightleftharpoons B$, takes place along n different (i.e. parallel) paths, for which *no* intermediates of any significant concentration are detectable (i.e. the concentrations of any intermediates are much less than the concentrations of A and B) then this counts as a single-step reaction and there is only one relaxation effect whose relaxation time is given as above.

If the reaction takes place in two or more steps, which may be parallel or successive and in which the concentrations of one or more intermediates are detectable (i.e. kinetically significant), then we obtain what is known as a *relaxation spectrum*. This means that if we were to plot reciprocal relaxation times for the system we would obtain characteristic values, in the same way that characteristic absorption lines appear in the i.r. spectrum

TABLE 2.1 Contributions to reciprocal relaxation time τ^{-1} for various half-reactions.

$A \xrightarrow{k_{12}}$ products	$\tau^{-1} = k_{12}$
$A + B \xrightarrow{k_{12}}$ products	$\tau^{-1} = k_{12}(\bar{c}_A + \bar{c}_B)$
$A + B + C \xrightarrow{k_{12}}$ products	$\tau^{-1} = k_{12}(\bar{c}_A\bar{c}_B + \bar{c}_B\bar{c}_C + \bar{c}_C\bar{c}_A)$
$2A \xrightarrow{k_{12}}$ products	$\tau^{-1} = 4k_{12}\bar{c}_A$
$A + B \xrightarrow{k_{12}}$ products (B is buffered)	$\tau^{-1} = k_{12}\bar{c}_B$
$A + B \xrightarrow{k_{12}}$ products + B (B is a catalyst)	$\tau^{-1} = k_{12}\bar{c}_B$

of a particular molecule. The order of the spectrum depends on the number of independent relaxation steps comprising the system, though not necessarily in a simple way, and as the number of steps increases so the complexity of the relaxation expression also increases. (A reason for the use of this spectroscopic terminology will become apparent as we derive the relaxation expression for a two-step reaction in which the individual relaxation times are similar in magnitude.) It is sometimes a little difficult to differentiate between a single-step and a multistep reaction, but if more than one relaxation effect is observed (or if an apparently single effect produced by a small perturbation is not a perfect exponential), the reaction is necessarily a multistep one. The reverse is not necessarily the case.

Let us consider a simple two-step mechanism

$$\underset{①}{A + B} \underset{k_{21}}{\overset{k_{12}}{\rightleftharpoons}} \underset{②}{AB} \underset{k_{32}}{\overset{k_{23}}{\rightleftharpoons}} \underset{③}{C} \tag{2.2}$$

in which the first step is much faster than the second. Such a system is characterized by two relaxation times [$=(n - 1)$, where n is the number of stoichiometrically identifiable states; it might be less than

$(n - 1)$ if some steps are degenerate]. After perturbation, the new equilibrium position of step ①–② will have been reached before step ②–③ has begun to relax. Therefore, ①–② can be considered in isolation and τ_{I}^{-1} is given simply by

$$\tau_{\mathrm{I}}^{-1} = k_{12}(\bar{c}_{\mathrm{A}} + \bar{c}_{\mathrm{B}}) + k_{21}$$

For the slower relaxation effect, τ_{II}^{-1} can be worked out in a similar way. The rate of production of C at displacement $\Delta\bar{c}_{\mathrm{C}}$ from the new equilibrium position is given by,

$$\frac{\mathrm{d}(\bar{c}_{\mathrm{C}} - \Delta\bar{c}_{\mathrm{C}})}{\mathrm{d}t} = k_{23}(\bar{c}_{\mathrm{AB}} - \Delta\bar{c}_{\mathrm{AB}}) - k_{32}(\bar{c}_{\mathrm{C}} - \Delta\bar{c}_{\mathrm{C}})$$

The equilibrium condition is

$$\frac{\mathrm{d}\bar{c}_{\mathrm{C}}}{\mathrm{d}t} = k_{23}\bar{c}_{\mathrm{AB}} - k_{32}\bar{c}_{\mathrm{C}}$$

Hence

$$\frac{\mathrm{d}\Delta\bar{c}_{\mathrm{C}}}{\mathrm{d}t} = k_{23}\Delta\bar{c}_{\mathrm{AB}} - k_{32}\Delta\bar{c}_{\mathrm{C}}$$

and we now have to express $\Delta\bar{c}_{\mathrm{AB}}$ in terms of $\Delta\bar{c}_{\mathrm{C}}$ so as to be able to write this expression in the form

$$\frac{\mathrm{d}\Delta\bar{c}_{\mathrm{X}}}{\mathrm{d}t} = -k\Delta\bar{c}_{\mathrm{X}}$$

The stoichiometric relationship (i.e. mass conservation expression) is

$$-\Delta\bar{c}_{\mathrm{A}} = -\Delta\bar{c}_{\mathrm{B}} = +(\Delta\bar{c}_{\mathrm{AB}} + \Delta\bar{c}_{\mathrm{C}})$$

and since the first step is always at equilibrium while the second step is relaxing,

$$k_{12}\bar{c}_{\mathrm{A}}\bar{c}_{\mathrm{B}} = k_{21}\bar{c}_{\mathrm{AB}}$$

Hence

$$k_{12}(\bar{c}_{\mathrm{A}} - \Delta\bar{c}_{\mathrm{A}})(\bar{c}_{\mathrm{B}} - \Delta\bar{c}_{\mathrm{B}}) = k_{21}(\bar{c}_{\mathrm{AB}} - \Delta\bar{c}_{\mathrm{AB}})$$

and if the displacement is small,

$$k_{12}(\bar{c}_{\mathrm{A}}\Delta\bar{c}_{\mathrm{B}} + \bar{c}_{\mathrm{B}}\Delta\bar{c}_{\mathrm{A}}) = k_{21}\Delta\bar{c}_{\mathrm{AB}}$$

Substituting:

$$-k_{12}(\bar{c}_{\mathrm{A}} + \bar{c}_{\mathrm{B}})(\Delta\bar{c}_{\mathrm{AB}} + \Delta\bar{c}_{\mathrm{C}}) = k_{21}\Delta\bar{c}_{\mathrm{AB}}$$

Therefore

$$\Delta\bar{c}_{\mathrm{AB}} = \frac{-k_{12}(\bar{c}_{\mathrm{A}} + \bar{c}_{\mathrm{B}})\Delta\bar{c}_{\mathrm{C}}}{k_{12}(\bar{c}_{\mathrm{A}} + \bar{c}_{\mathrm{B}}) + k_{21}}$$

and

$$\frac{\mathrm{d}\Delta\bar{c}_{\mathrm{C}}}{\mathrm{d}t} = \frac{-k_{12}k_{23}(\bar{c}_{\mathrm{A}} + \bar{c}_{\mathrm{B}})\Delta\bar{c}_{\mathrm{C}}}{k_{12}(\bar{c}_{\mathrm{A}} + \bar{c}_{\mathrm{B}}) + k_{21}} - k_{32}\Delta\bar{c}_{\mathrm{C}}$$

giving

$$\tau_{\mathrm{II}}^{-1} = \frac{k_{12}k_{23}(\bar{c}_{\mathrm{A}} + \bar{c}_{\mathrm{B}})}{k_{12}(\bar{c}_{\mathrm{A}} + \bar{c}_{\mathrm{B}}) + k_{21}} + k_{32}$$

As we would have expected, τ_{II}^{-1} consists of the sum of two terms: a simple first-order term k_{32} (unmodified, since the concentration of C is not directly affected by equilibrium ①–②) and a modified first-order term involving k_{23} (the modifying factor taking account of the rapid pre-equilibrium).

The situation is rather less straightforward if the characteristic rates of the two reactions are similar. Instead of there being two independent relaxation effects, there is an interaction between the two resulting in what might be called two 'normal modes'. Let us see how the relaxation times for reaction (2.2) are modified if the rates of the two steps are comparable.

Since we still have two relaxation times we shall require two differential equations to describe the system. We shall take $\mathrm{d}\Delta\bar{c}_{\mathrm{A}}/\mathrm{d}t$ and $\mathrm{d}\Delta\bar{c}_{\mathrm{AB}}/\mathrm{d}t$ and express them as two simultaneous equations in $\Delta\bar{c}_{\mathrm{A}}$ and $\Delta\bar{c}_{\mathrm{AB}}$, though we could equally well have used $\mathrm{d}\Delta\bar{c}_{\mathrm{B}}/\mathrm{d}t$ and $\mathrm{d}\Delta\bar{c}_{\mathrm{C}}/\mathrm{d}t$ with $\Delta\bar{c}_{\mathrm{B}}$ and $\Delta\bar{c}_{\mathrm{C}}$. Applying the method outlined above we obtain,

$$\frac{\mathrm{d}\Delta\bar{c}_{\mathrm{A}}}{\mathrm{d}t} = -k_{12}(\bar{c}_{\mathrm{A}} + \bar{c}_{\mathrm{B}})\Delta\bar{c}_{\mathrm{A}} + k_{21}\Delta\bar{c}_{\mathrm{AB}} \tag{2.3}$$

and

$$\frac{\mathrm{d}\Delta\bar{c}_{\mathrm{AB}}}{\mathrm{d}t} = k_{12}(\bar{c}_{\mathrm{A}} + \bar{c}_{\mathrm{B}})\Delta\bar{c}_{\mathrm{A}} - (k_{21} + k_{23})\Delta\bar{c}_{\mathrm{AB}} + k_{32}\Delta\bar{c}_{\mathrm{C}}$$

Mass conservation (stoichiometry) allows the substitution

$$\Delta\bar{c}_{\mathrm{C}} = -(\Delta\bar{c}_{\mathrm{A}} + \Delta\bar{c}_{\mathrm{AB}})$$

and hence we can write

$$\frac{\mathrm{d}\Delta\bar{c}_{\mathrm{AB}}}{\mathrm{d}t} = [k_{12}(\bar{c}_{\mathrm{A}} + \bar{c}_{\mathrm{B}}) - k_{32}]\Delta\bar{c}_{\mathrm{A}} - (k_{21} + k_{23} + k_{32})\Delta\bar{c}_{\mathrm{AB}} \tag{2.4}$$

Equations (2.3) and (2.4) are of the form

$$-\frac{\mathrm{d}\Delta\bar{c}_{\mathrm{A}}}{\mathrm{d}t} = a_{11}\Delta\bar{c}_{\mathrm{A}} + a_{12}\Delta\bar{c}_{\mathrm{AB}}$$

$$-\frac{\mathrm{d}\Delta\bar{c}_{\mathrm{AB}}}{\mathrm{d}t} = a_{21}\Delta\bar{c}_{\mathrm{A}} + a_{22}\Delta\bar{c}_{\mathrm{AB}}$$

and they have to be transformed in order to be able to express the relaxation times in terms of the rate constants. In other words, they have to be written in the form

$$\frac{d\Delta\bar{c}_1}{dt} = -(\tau_I^{-1})\Delta\bar{c}_1 \quad \text{and} \quad \frac{d\Delta\bar{c}_2}{dt} = -(\tau_{II}^{-1})\Delta\bar{c}_2$$

If we make the substitutions

$$\frac{d\Delta\bar{c}_A}{dt} = -\tau^{-1}\Delta\bar{c}_A \quad \text{and} \quad \frac{d\Delta\bar{c}_{AB}}{dt} = -\tau^{-1}\Delta\bar{c}_{AB}$$

into equations (2.3) and (2.4), we obtain the following simultaneous equations:

$$\tau^{-1}\Delta\bar{c}_A = a_{11}\Delta\bar{c}_A + a_{12}\Delta\bar{c}_{AB}$$

$$\tau^{-1}\Delta\bar{c}_{AB} = a_{21}\Delta\bar{c}_A + a_{22}\Delta\bar{c}_{AB}$$

These may be solved for τ^{-1} after eliminating $\Delta\bar{c}_A$ and $\Delta\bar{c}_{AB}$, to give

$$\tau^{-2} - \tau^{-1}(a_{11} + a_{22}) + (a_{11}a_{22} - a_{12}a_{21}) = 0$$

The two reciprocal relaxation times τ_I^{-1} and τ_{II}^{-1} are then

$$\frac{(a_{11} + a_{22}) \pm \sqrt{(a_{11} + a_{22})^2 - 4(a_{11}a_{22} - a_{12}a_{21})}}{2}$$

where τ_I^{-1} represents the sum and τ_{II}^{-1} represents the difference of the two terms. (Such a manipulation can also be accomplished readily in terms of matrix algebra since it corresponds to an affine coordination transformation. This approach is discussed briefly in Appendix C.)

In this particular case (e.g. the binding of an inhibitor to an enzyme followed by a conformational change), the individual rate constants can all be evaluated.

The product of the reciprocal relaxation times,

$$(\tau_I\tau_{II})^{-1} = (a_{11}a_{22} - a_{12}a_{21})$$
$$= k_{12}(k_{23} + k_{32})(\bar{c}_A + \bar{c}_B) + k_{21}k_{32}$$

Thus a plot of $(\tau_I\tau_{II})^{-1}$ *versus* $(\bar{c}_A + \bar{c}_B)$ has a slope of $k_{12}(k_{23} + k_{32})$ and an intercept of $k_{21}k_{32}$ (Figure 2.10(*a*)). The sum of the reciprocal relaxation times,

$$\tau_I^{-1} + \tau_{II}^{-1} = (a_{11} + a_{22})$$
$$= k_{12}(\bar{c}_A + \bar{c}_B) + k_{21} + k_{23} + k_{32}$$

Hence a plot of $(\tau_I^{-1} + \tau_{II}^{-1})$ *versus* $(\bar{c}_A + \bar{c}_B)$ has a slope of k_{12} and an intercept of $(k_{21} + k_{23} + k_{32})$ (Figure 2.10(*b*)).

We might reemphasize that under the conditions we have just been discussing each of the relaxation effects contains a contribution from the two reactions. The relaxation effects are normal modes in the sense that i.r. spectral lines of polyatomic molecules are associated with the normal vibrational modes rather than the vibration of any particular bond. Although the two relaxation times are close to one another when the characteristic rates of the two steps are similar, from a practical point of view they can only be determined precisely if there is a certain minimum separation (unless they can be separated by using different wavelengths).

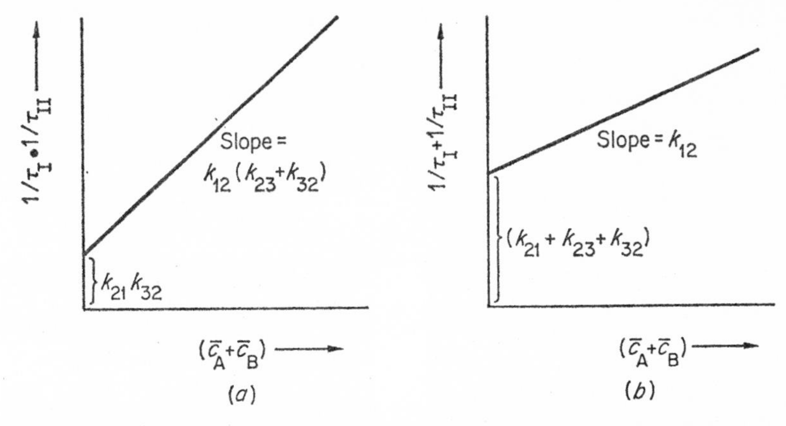

FIGURE 2.10 Determination of rate constants from reciprocal relaxation times for reaction (2.2) in which τ_{I} and τ_{II} have comparable values.

This minimum separation depends on the relative magnitudes of the relaxation effects and on the technique being used to determine τ, but typically it is such that $\tau_{\mathrm{II}}/\tau_{\mathrm{I}}$ must be greater than about three. It is sometimes possible to increase this ratio by adjusting the concentrations or, since the different steps will often have different activation parameters, by altering the temperature.

As the complexity of the chemical system increases, so do the expressions for the various relaxation times. The principles used in the determination of them, however, remain the same and, as we have seen, it is often possible to evaluate the actual rate constants by a suitable choice of conditions and of the variables which are plotted. Before discussing the experimental methods of evaluating relaxation times we shall allude briefly to a system in which chemical relaxation was used to reveal a second reaction where equilibrium studies had suggested the presence of only a single reaction.

The dye Biebrich Scarlet (BS)(I) binds to the proteolytic enzyme α-chymotrypsin (CT) near its active site and there is a small spectral

HO

$^{-}O_3S$—⟨⟩—N=N—⟨⟩—N=N—⟨⟩

SO_3^-

(I)

change which, as a result of equilibrium studies, was associated with the formation of the 1 : 1 complex,

$$\text{BS} + \text{CT} \rightleftharpoons \text{BS}\,.\,\text{CT} \tag{2.5}$$

The spectrum of this system is slightly temperature-sensitive and so it might be expected that a single relaxation effect associated with this reaction would be seen on submitting the system to a temperature-jump

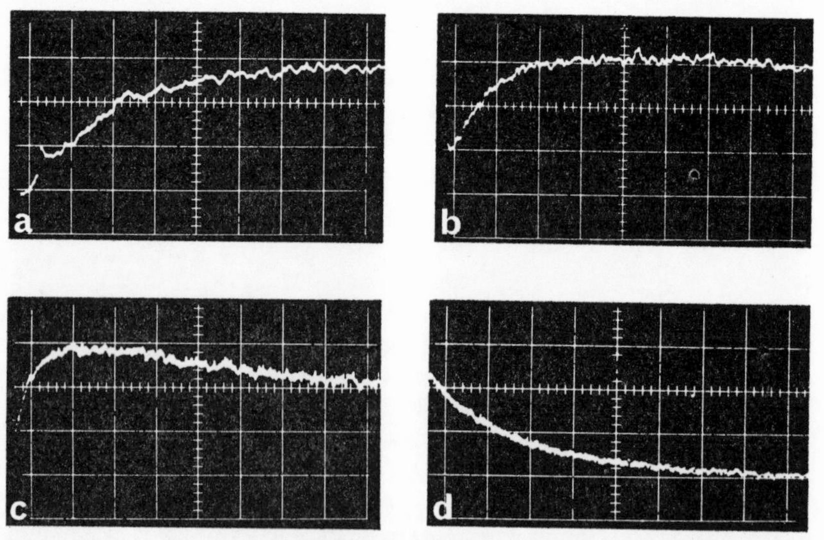

FIGURE 2.11 Relaxation spectrum for the BS/CT system (total concentrations $1{\cdot}0 \times 10^{-4}$ and $8{\cdot}0 \times 10^{-4}$ M, respectively). Time bases are (*a*) 10 μsec, (*b*) 20 μsec, (*c*) 50 μsec and (*d*) 500 μsec per large division, and the sensitivity (vertical scale) is the same in each case.

(see below). However, two large opposing effects are observed—as shown in Figure 2.11—with the final absorbance not very different from the initial absorbance. We are seeing two coupled reactions, the major contribution to τ_{I} being from the dimerization of (I) and that to τ_{II} being from the binding of the monomer to the enzyme (reaction (2.5)). Thus, by introducing the dimension of time, it is possible to show that what on the basis of equilibrium studies appears to be a small single reaction (represented by (2.5)) is in fact two much larger opposing reactions.

This ability to spread the reactions out along the time axis is a particularly valuable feature of relaxation techniques, and indeed of many of the fast reaction techniques being discussed in this book. We shall return to this point in Chapter 4 since it is especially relevant in an investigation of enzyme and other complex reactions. We shall not consider in this chapter specific reactions which have been studied by relaxation techniques since many of those quoted in Chapters 3 and 4 have been followed this way.

The determination of the relaxation time

We have discussed relaxation techniques in rather general terms, assuming that it is possible somehow to displace an equilibrium, but we have not considered the methods by which the relaxation time can be obtained.

Suppose that reaction (2.1) has a finite standard enthalpy change ΔH° associated with it. This implies that the equilibrium constant K, and hence the position of the equilibrium, is dependent on the temperature T, since

$$(\partial \ln K/\partial(1/T))_P = -\Delta H^\circ/R$$

A sudden rise of 10° in the temperature of the solution would therefore cause a change in, say, the optical absorbance due to C as more C is produced (or used up, depending on whether the reaction is endo- or exothermic). Measurement of the optical density of the solution will yield directly a curve such as that shown by the full line in Figure 2.9. This is the so-called *temperature-jump*, or T-jump technique, and the sudden increase in temperature can be produced by discharging the electrical energy stored in a condenser through the reaction solution. The solution, whose volume may be as small as one or two millilitres, is placed in a cell between two specially shaped electrodes[18] which have been designed to produce a near-uniform field (Figure 2.12). If the reaction mixture is not a sufficiently good electrical conductor an inert electrolyte such as 0·1 M potassium nitrate must be added to carry the current and thus ensure rapid heating. Spectrophotometric observation at a given wavelength is made at right angles to the cell axis (Figure 2.13). A typical relaxation curve, as displayed on an oscilloscope, is shown in Figure 2.11(*a*) and (*d*). The relaxation time may be derived from a semilogarithmic plot or by comparison with standard exponential curves. If the chemical system

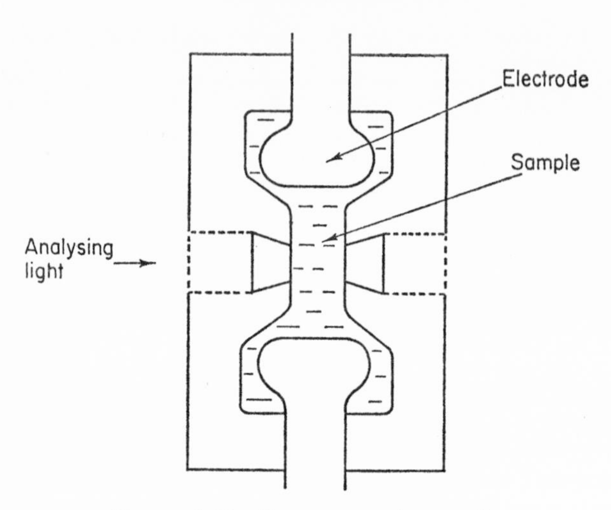

FIGURE 2.12 Temperature-jump cell.

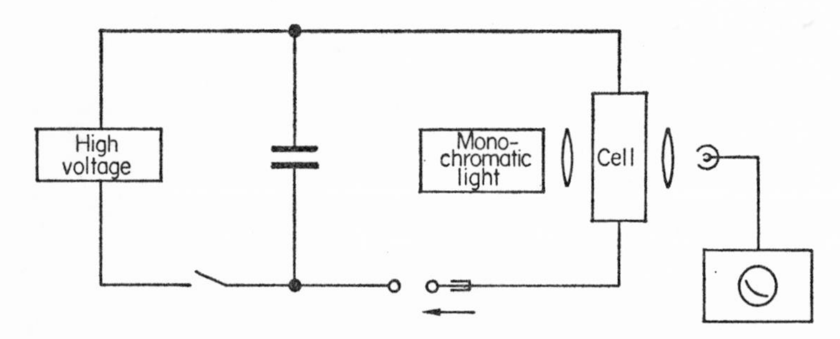

FIGURE 2.13 Schematic diagram of temperature-jump method which uses electrical discharge for heating solution.

reacts but apparently does not relax (e.g. if the reactions are faster than the response time of the instrument, which is usually a few microseconds) a simple step-function is observed (cf. Figure 2.9, curve 2). If no reaction occurs on T-jumping then evidently there is no change in optical density (cf. Figure 2.9, curve 1). An alternative approach to the problem of suddenly raising the temperature is to use a pulse of microwaves. The advantage of this method is that non-conducting solutions may be used, though only a relatively small temperature rise can be obtained, generally less than 1°. A Q-switched laser (cf. p. 22) has also been used as the heat source. By combining flow and T-jump techniques it is possible to study the reactions of species in quasi-equilibrium.[19]

The *pressure-jump* method[20] uses a sudden change of pressure to displace the equilibrium. The sensitivity of a reaction to pressure depends on the change in volume ΔV° and is represented quantitatively by the equation

$$(\partial \ln K/\partial P)_T = -\Delta V^\circ/RT$$

The sample is placed in a flexible cell which is contained in a pressure-vessel filled with an inert liquid such as xylene. A pressure of about 65 atmospheres is set up in the vessel and this is reduced to atmospheric pressure within about 10^{-4} sec by puncturing a thin metal disc set into the wall of the vessel. The attainment of the new equilibrium is followed conductimetrically. An alternative method is to place the cell containing the reaction sample in a liquid-filled shock tube (see p. 29) and to use light absorption for following the reaction. The reason that the T-jump technique has found wider application than P-jump (besides being able to follow faster reactions) is that the displacement of a typical reaction produced by a 10° temperature rise is considerably greater than that produced by a 65 atmosphere pressure change. Thus, if $\Delta T = 10°$ and $T = 300°K$, then for a ΔH° as small as 1 kcal/mole the ratio of the equilibrium constants at the two temperatures is about 1·06, i.e. there is an approximately 6% change in the equilibrium constant. The corresponding displacement for a pressure change of 65 atmospheres only comes if ΔV° is about 22 cm^3/mole. This is a relatively high value and is only found in reactions in which there is a considerable change in the electrostrictive effects of the reactants and products on the solvent, for example, if there is a charge neutralization. Thus ΔV° is 22 cm^3/mole for $H^+ + OH^- \rightleftharpoons H_2O$. On the other hand, most reactions have values of ΔH° considerably greater than 1 kcal/mole.

The *electric field-jump* technique[21] is applicable for reactions which are associated with a change in dipole moment, for example, the dimerization of carboxylic acids in non-polar solvents:

```
                 O·····H—O
               //         \
2RCOOH ⇌ R—C               C—R
               \          //
                O—H·····O
```

A square electric field pulse of about 100 kV/cm with a rise time of a fraction of a microsecond can be obtained by discharging a 300 m long high voltage cable through the cell. This technique, which can be used to measure relaxation times down to 10^{-7} sec, has not yet been used very widely because of the considerable experimental difficulties in constructing the apparatus. It has the advantage over present-day T-jump instruments in that it can measure shorter times, and it is being used to follow reactions, such as the binding of dye molecules to micelles, which are models for reactions involved in nerve action.

So far we have considered step-function relaxation methods in which a single pulse is applied across the equilibrium system and the consequent rapid adjustment of the concentrations is followed. Another group of relaxation methods, the *stationary methods*, are also used in which a steadily oscillating function is applied across the solution. Because of

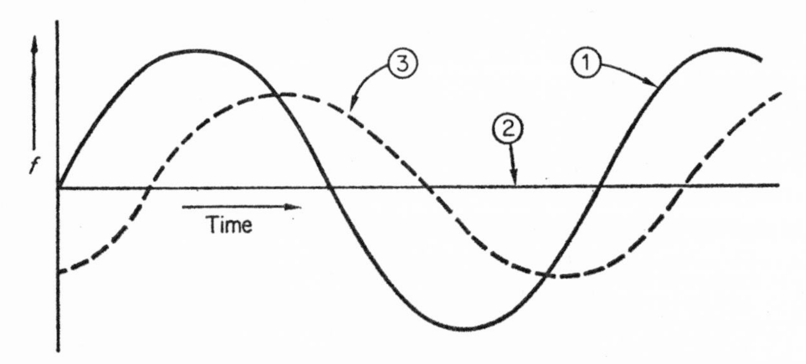

FIGURE 2.14 Chemical relaxation with a periodic forcing function.

chemical relaxation the system does not follow directly the disturbing function but lags some way behind it—rather as the current passing through an inductance lags behind the applied a.c. voltage across its ends.

In Figure 2.14 we represent the forcing function (i.e. the oscillating disturbance) by curve 1. If the frequency of the forcing function is sufficiently low, the system can readjust itself rapidly and the concentration changes can effectively keep up with their equilibrium values. In this case, the concentrations are also given by curve 1. If, on the other hand, the frequency of the forcing function is much too high for the system to readjust itself, there will be no observed concentration changes, as indicated by curve 2. The interesting situation occurs when the applied frequency is of the same order of magnitude as the rate at which the changing chemical equilibrium can be set up in the system. In this case, represented by curve 3, there is an interaction between the system and the forcing function in which energy is absorbed by the system. We can determine the relaxation time by analysing this phase-lag and amplitude loss.

A time-independent 'transfer function' $\mathfrak{S}$ has been introduced[16] which, like the forcing function, can be treated mathematically in terms of a complex exponential. Although it is not necessary to consider these functions in detail for the practical applications of the stationary relaxation methods, it is interesting to note the connection between the transfer function and the measured quantities. It is possible to obtain the relaxation time in two general ways. One method uses the real part of the transfer function $\mathfrak{S}_{re}$, whose variation with the applied circular frequency ω is shown in Figure 2.15(*a*). The relaxation time corresponds to the value of ω at which the modulus of the tangent to the curve has its maximum value. A physical property which shows a frequency dependence of this type is the velocity of sound. This frequency dependence is called sound dispersion, and so it is common to call the methods which use the real component of the transfer function *dispersion methods*. The imaginary part of the transfer function $\mathfrak{S}_{im}$ has a frequency dependence of the type shown in Figure 2.15(*b*). It represents the amount of energy transferred to the system per period of oscillation owing to the relaxation; and the relaxation time corresponds to the frequency at which the greatest interaction occurs. Methods which use the imaginary component of the transfer function all involve the measurement of energy absorption and are therefore called *absorption methods*. (It is interesting to note that the same possibilities exist with all resonance systems. Thus in n.m.r. spectroscopy, for example, the position of resonance can be measured either from the real or the imaginary part of the interaction function. In this case the measurement is normally made in the v-mode, corresponding to the imaginary part which is 90° out-of-phase with the rotating magnetic field H_1 (see p. 49) although it could equally well be made in the u-mode, corresponding to the real part which is in-phase with H_1.)

In principle, as for the transient methods, any parameter which causes a measurable displacement in the chemical equilibrium under investigation may be used as the forcing function. Thus, a high-frequency oscillating electric field might be used with solutions of weak electrolytes or an alternating magnetic field with systems in which there is a difference in magnetic moment between the reactants and the products. But because of the very small effects expected and the considerable experimental difficulties in measuring them, techniques which make use of these properties are not yet well developed. The most widely used stationary method uses the disturbance caused by high-frequency sound-waves, and we shall consider briefly the application of this *ultrasonic* method to the study of chemical relaxation.

When sound-waves are propagated adiabatically through a liquid, alternating regions of high and low pressure are produced which are associated with slight increases and decreases of temperature. If a chemical system is present in which the position of equilibrium is pressure- or temperature-sensitive, the disturbance caused by the sound-waves may be used as a forcing function. (It does not matter whether, in a given case, the

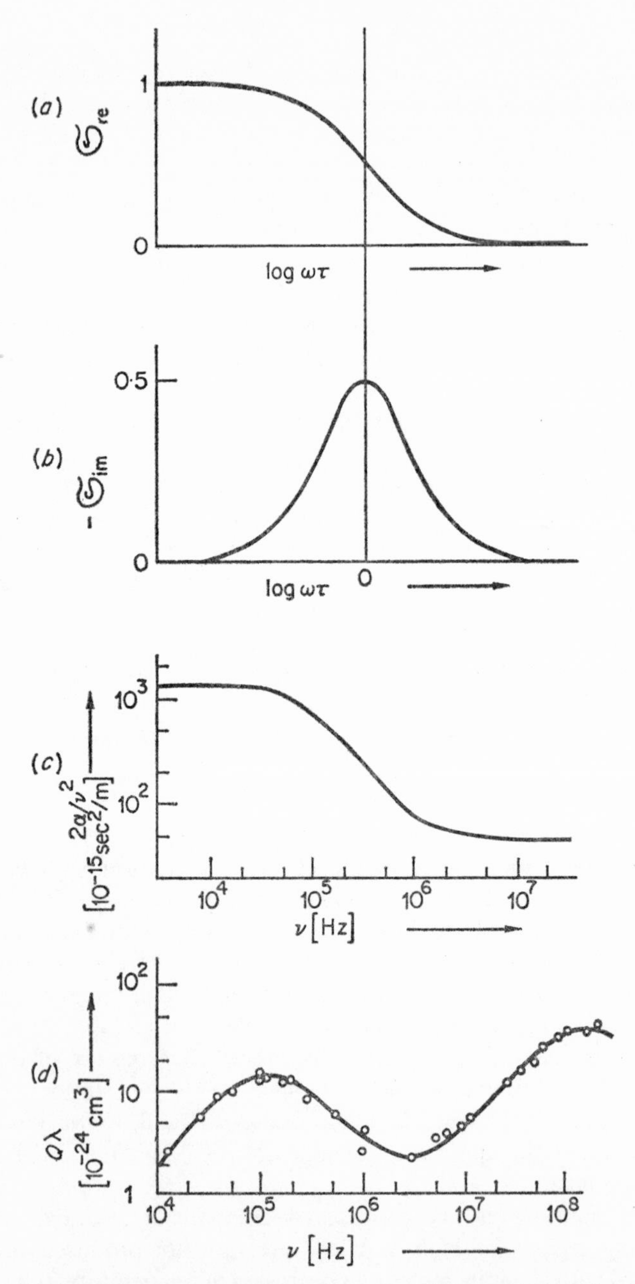

FIGURE 2.15 Real (*a*) and imaginary (*b*) parts of transfer function and the variation with frequency ν for aqueous $MgSO_4$ at 20° of $2\alpha/\nu^2$ (curve (*c*), Ref. 22(a) for 0·014 M solution) and $Q\lambda$ (curve (*d*), Ref. 22(b) for 10^{-2}–10^{-1} M solutions).

system is responding to the pressure or temperature changes since the two are completely coupled.)

The attenuation constant α is a measure of the energy absorbed when a sound wave is passed through a liquid (the decrease in energy for a plane sound wave propagated in the x-direction is given by a factor $e^{-2\alpha x}$). It is made up of several contributions, the number depending on the number of discrete relaxation phenomena n in the system. Thus

$$\alpha = \sum_{n} \alpha_{\mathrm{chem},n} + \alpha_{\mathrm{res}}$$

where $\alpha_{\mathrm{chem},n}$ is that part of the attenuation constant attributable to the nth chemical relaxation process, while α_{res} is the residual attenuation associated with the solvent and inherent in the design of the apparatus. The plot of α/ν^2 against log ν has the typical step form, as shown in Figure 2.15(c). The residual attenuation, which may include a relaxation effect which is too fast to show up as a distinct step, is often determined in a separate experiment on the solvent alone, although strictly speaking α_{res} need not be the same for the pure solvent as for the solution (for example an electrolyte may alter α_{res} by tending to break up the highly hydrogen-bonded water structure). A plot of log ($Q\lambda$) against log ν has the peaked form, as shown in Figure 2.15(d). Q is the chemical absorption cross-section and is defined as $Q = 2\alpha_{\mathrm{chem}}/N_{\mathrm{A}}c_i^0$ where N_{A} is the Avogadro number, c_i^0 is the concentration of species i, and λ is the sound wavelength. The number of separate peaks is equal to the number of discrete relaxation effects and $1/\tau = \omega_{\mathrm{max}}$.

Several experimental methods have been used to measure the attenuation of sound waves and one of the simplest employs an optical technique based on the Debye–Sears effect. A progressive sound wave of known frequency is generated in the liquid sample by means of a quartz crystal set into the bottom of the glass container and excited by a high-frequency generator (Figure 2.16). The refractive index of a liquid is dependent on the pressure so, to a parallel light beam passing through the vessel perpendicular to the plane of the wavefront, the alternating regions of high and low pressure behave like a diffraction grating. This arrangement can be used either to determine the dispersion or the energy absorption of the solution. Thus, the spacing of the diffraction orders depends on the wavelength, which is a dispersion characteristic, and the light intensity in the diffraction orders is a measure of the energy absorbed by the solution. This is because an increase in the intensity of the sound-wave forces more light from the zero diffraction order into the higher orders, i.e. the diffraction lines become more opaque. Light in the first diffraction order is separated by a slit[22] and its intensity measured with a photomultiplier;

it is assumed that the intensities of the higher orders are sufficiently low that the approximation may be made that the measured intensity is proportional to the sound-pressure level. The pressure level is determined at different distances from the sound source by moving the light beam vertically. In practice the cell is usually moved through a fixed light beam and the photomultiplier signal is amplified and recorded on a pen recorder. To avoid the difficulties associated with the continuous illumination of the photomultiplier a pulsed-light signal is used. This is achieved elegantly by using a periodically pulsed excitation of the quartz crystal.

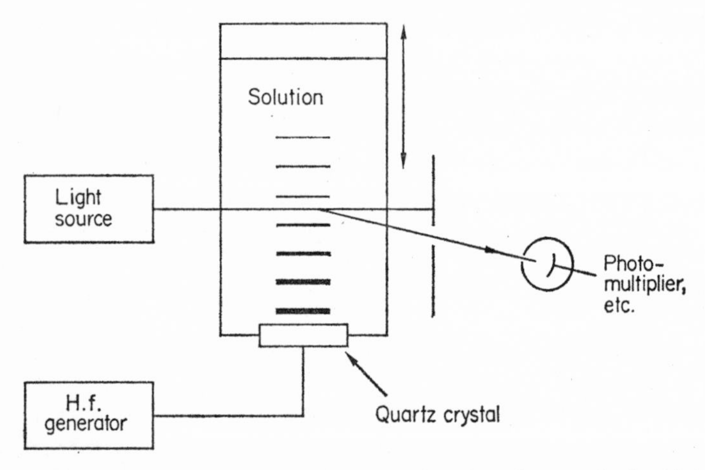

FIGURE 2.16 Schematic diagram of ultrasonic relaxation method which uses the Debye–Sears effect to measure the sound attenuation.

Ultrasonic techniques have been used to measure relaxation times in several types of system, for example, metal complex formation and proton transfer. The advantage over the temperature-jump method is that shorter relaxation times can be measured, but there are two severe disadvantages. In the first place, the absorption is unspecific. It is often difficult to know which chemical reaction is causing it since the change in physical property due to a single identifiable species is not being used in the analysis. In the second place, most experimental arrangements require large volumes of highly concentrated solution. Both difficulties make it rather unsuited to the study of biological systems. From a historic standpoint the method is interesting in that it was the first chemical relaxation technique to be applied, albeit somewhat accidentally. In the late 1940's and early 1950's the possibility was being investigated of using ultrasonics to measure the depth of water beneath a ship. Calculation and preliminary experiments on brine suggested that the method was feasible but when the apparatus was tested in sea water it was found that there were certain frequencies at which the signal could not be picked up. Some component of sea water other than H_2O and NaCl was presumably absorbing the sound. It was discovered[22] that one of the principal absorbers in sea water is magnesium sulphate and that the chemical relaxation associated with the formation of the $MgSO_4$ complex (Chapter 3) is what attenuates the sound.

COMPETITION METHODS: SPECTRAL LINE BROADENING, ETC.

It frequently happens that the various species involved in an equilibrium have different u.v., visible or i.r. spectra. In that case, we expect to see absorption peaks corresponding to both species but, if δt is the lifetime of each species (assuming for the present that they exist in equal amounts and, therefore, that δt is the same for both), the Uncertainty Principle leads us to expect a broadening of the absorption lines $\delta \nu$ given by $\delta \nu \simeq 1/(2\pi\delta t)$ where ν is in frequency units. The frequencies associated with these spectra are high (of the order of 10^{13}–10^{15} sec^{-1}) so the broadening cannot be appreciable unless δt is less than about 10^{-13} sec, which it usually is not. Because the resolving power of u.v., visible or i.r. spectrometers is insufficient to detect the very small broadening, this method is usually unsuitable for estimating δt. With n.m.r. spectroscopy, however, the frequency used for detection is smaller by a factor of 10^6 and the spectral lines are often of the order of 1 Hz (sec^{-1}) in width. Because the lines associated with equilibrating species may be only a few sec^{-1} apart, very marked broadening may occur even when the lifetimes are as long as 10^{-3}–10^{-1} sec. (If their lifetimes are much shorter than this, the two forms will give a single narrow peak and therefore be indistinguishable.)

It will be apparent that the situation here is similar to that obtaining in ultrasonics and other periodic relaxation methods. If the characteristic time of the chemical reaction is similar in magnitude to the characteristic time of the physical process (in this case given by the reciprocal difference in frequency between the absorption peaks, although we shall amplify this below) then we can derive information about the kinetics of the chemical process from its modification of the physical phenomenon. Several spectroscopic and other methods have been used in this way to study chemical kinetics. We shall discuss the use of n.m.r. first and in greater detail than the others partly because it has been (and probably will continue to be) more widely used and partly because the theory of its application is more fully developed. It has the added advantage of being applicable to the study of virtual reactions, in which the reactant and product are identical.

(a) The use of nuclear magnetic resonance

We shall give an outline of the n.m.r. phenomenon and then an account of the way in which it can be modified by chemical exchange. Further details may be obtained from one of the standard texts[23] and several authors, notably Johnson,[24] have given a fuller treatment of the application of n.m.r. to kinetics. No discussion will be given of the kinetic application of n.m.r. in which it is used merely to measure concentrations.

The n.m.r. phenomenon

A nucleus whose mass number and charge are both even (effectively, one with a mass number which is a multiple of 4, e.g. ^{12}C, ^{16}O, ^{32}S) has no spin. Other nuclei may have spin values I equal to multiples of $\frac{1}{2}$, associated with magnetic quantum numbers $m = I, (I - 1), \ldots, -I$. A spinning nucleus has a rotating charge which generates a magnetic field and consequently has a nuclear magnetic moment μ. In the absence of an applied magnetic field the spinning nucleus has no preferred direction of alignment, but when it experiences an external magnetic field a nucleus of spin $\frac{1}{2}$ can take up only two positions. (We shall confine our discussion to the simplest case, the proton, although similar considerations apply to other nuclei with finite spin.[24]) For $m = +\frac{1}{2}$ it is aligned in the direction of the field H_0 and at an angle θ to it (Figure 2.17), while for $m = -\frac{1}{2}$ it is aligned at an angle θ against the applied field. The situation $m = +\frac{1}{2}$ corresponds to a lower energy than $m = -\frac{1}{2}$ (Figure 2.18) and the energy difference ΔE is proportional to the strength of the applied field H_0. The equation $\Delta E = h\nu$, where ν is the frequency of absorption (see below) is often written in terms of the nuclear g-factor g_N and the nuclear magneton β_N ($=(e\hbar/2Mc)$, where e is the charge on the nucleus, $\hbar$ is $h/2\pi$, M is the mass and c the velocity of light), thus $h\nu = g_N\beta_N H_0$ (β_N is constant and g_N is the quantity which distinguishes one nucleus from another). In view of this difference in energy between the two levels, we would expect their populations to be different. The equilibrium ratio of the numbers of protons in the two levels can be calculated by means of the Boltzmann distribution law: $N_\beta/N_\alpha = e^{-\Delta E/kT}$. At normal temperatures and moderately high fields (thousands of gauss) this is only about 5 parts per million. In n.m.r. spectroscopy the nuclei are made to change from one state to the other and the conditions under which these transfers occur are measured. As we shall see, the fact that this equilibrium distribution is set up at all and the way in which it is achieved are of considerable importance to the measurement of rate constants by n.m.r. (and other spectroscopic methods). For the moment, let us assume that thermal equilibrium exists, so that there are slightly more protons with spin α than spin β.

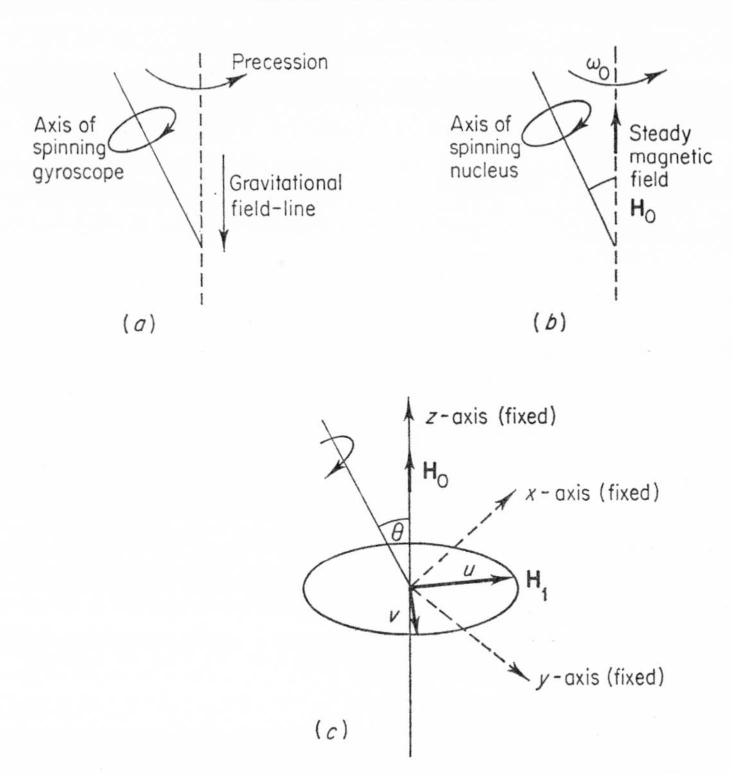

FIGURE 2.17 The precession of a spinning gyroscope in a gravitational field (*a*) and of a spinning nucleus in a magnetic field (*b*) and (*c*). The natural precession frequency of the nucleus is the Larmor frequency ω_0. The r.f. field $\mathbf{H}_1$ is applied in the transverse (x, y) plane and it rotates with frequency ω.

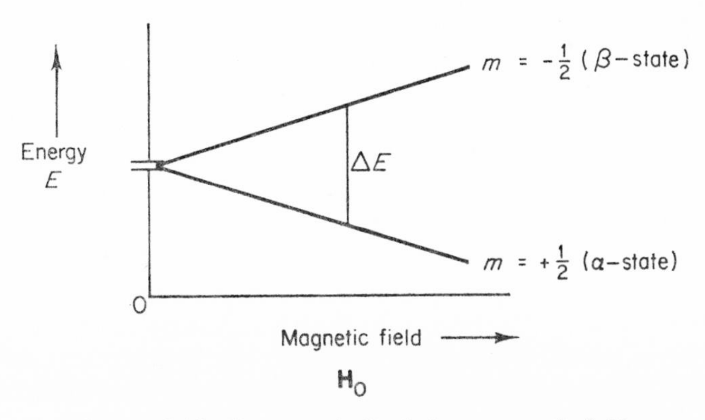

FIGURE 2.18 Proton spin levels in a magnetic field.

Although the analogy is in some ways unsatisfactory, it is interesting to compare the behaviour of a spinning nucleus in a magnetic field with that of a spinning gyroscope in a gravitational field (Figure 2.17). When the axis of the gyroscope lies along the earth's gravitational field lines it is found that there is zero relative motion about the other two axes. If the gyroscope is tilted about one of these other axes the displaced spin-axis begins to revolve slowly about the gravitational field line. Such precession is a direct consequence of the Principle of Conservation of Angular Momentum. A nucleus with magnetic moment μ situated in a magnetic field $\mathbf{H}_0$ behaves in a similar way. Because the magnetic moment vector is aligned automatically at an angle to $\mathbf{H}_0$, precession occurs about the field axis. The angular velocity of precession ω_0, called the natural or *Larmor frequency*, is directly proportional to $\mathbf{H}_0$. The spinning nucleus may be induced to change its spin quantum number if it interacts with a magnetic field rotating about the same axis provided the rotating field has the same frequency (ω_0) and phase as the nucleus. Consequently, an oscillating magnetic field $\mathbf{H}_1$ (which can be thought of as having a component moving in the same sense as the precessing nucleus) is applied perpendicular to the fixed magnetic field $\mathbf{H}_0$. The frequency of $\mathbf{H}_1$, ω, is varied until it coincides with the precession frequency ω_0. (In practice it is easier to keep ω fixed and to vary the steady magnetic field $\mathbf{H}_0$. This has the effect of varying the precession frequency ω_0.) The population difference between the two levels is important because the oscillating field is equally likely to produce transitions up from α to β as it is down from β to α, and we can only detect absorption of energy from the applied field if there are more α spins than β spins.

Two protons will precess at the same angular velocity only when the magnetic field strengths at their nuclei are the same. In any situation of chemical interest they are bonded to other species and the applied magnetic field is shielded to some extent by the bonding electrons and further modified by the other charged parts of the molecule. In a molecule containing two or more non-equivalent protons, therefore, the n.m.r. peaks do not come at the same place and the difference between the two positions (or their positions relative to a standard) is called the *chemical shift* δ. If the sensitivity of measurement is high it is often found that the peaks have a fine structure. This may arise from an interaction between the protons on neighbouring atoms, which results in a splitting of the energy levels of the spin states. The magnitude of this splitting, or *spin–spin interaction* J, is independent of the frequency ω and the background field $\mathbf{H}_0$.

We have indicated that the resonance absorption can only be detected if there is a population difference between the two spin levels. Let us investigate this proposition further.

Nuclear relaxation

So far, the only mechanism we have considered by which the magnetic quantum number may be changed involves the interaction between the precessing nucleus and an externally applied oscillating magnetic field of the same, or approximately the same, frequency. If this were the only path for the transference of energy, normal resonance would not be observed since energy would cease to be absorbed when the numbers of nuclei in the upper and lower states had been equalized. This equalization of the populations is termed *saturation* and it can be shown, by applying time-dependent perturbation theory, that the population difference (N_α–N_β) decays exponentially as the system becomes saturated. It is therefore necessary for the species in their excited states to be continually losing their excess energy to the surroundings by some form of radiationless transfer so that further absorption of energy can occur. This transfer of energy occurs by means of *nuclear relaxation*, which is exactly analogous to chemical relaxation (page 31) in that it is a kinetically first-order process and the relaxation time is the time taken for the population difference to drop to $1/e$ of its original value. A large number of factors such as molecular tumbling and local field inhomogeneities contribute to the nuclear relaxation, but it is usual to treat it in terms of two times, T_1 the *spin–lattice* (or *longitudinal*) and T_2 the *spin–spin* (or *transverse*) relaxation time.

The requirements for nuclear relaxation can be summarized as follows. In the first place there should be some direct interaction between a magnetic or electric field and the spins, and in the second place this field should be time-dependent. It should oscillate at, or approximately at, the Larmor frequency ω_0 since fields which do not oscillate or which oscillate at a frequency much less than ω_0 will not produce relaxation but will merely add to the general field in the neighbourhood of the proton—i.e. produce a change in the chemical shift. Fields which oscillate much more rapidly than ω_0 are also ineffective. The nuclear resonance frequency is typically 10^7 Hz, so electronic motions and molecular vibrations (typically 10^{11} and 10^{13} Hz, respectively) are usually relatively unimportant in producing nuclear relaxation (although the case of the paramagnetic ion Mn^{2+} is particularly interesting in that it has an unusually long electron-spin relaxation time and the electronic relaxation can therefore contribute significantly to the proton relaxation in a molecule in its neighbourhood).

In liquids there is continuous motion of the surroundings or lattice (namely any degree of freedom which is not involved in the specific spin system) and the spin–lattice relaxation time T_1 is a measure of the time taken for the nucleus to exchange energy with the molecules constituting the lattice.

In terms of Figure 2.17, T_1 is the time constant of the transitions along the longitudinal axis and, since the fixed magnetic field $\mathbf{H}_0$ is applied along this axis, it is not difficult to see intuitively why T_1 should be related to the saturation process. T_2 is the time constant of the transitions perpendicular to the fixed magnetic field $\mathbf{H}_0$ and it may or may not be equal to T_1. (The introduction of two relaxation times may appear rather arbitrary, but T_1 and T_2 actually come from the *Bloch equations*,[25] which are phenomenological representations of the shape of the n.m.r. absorption line. The Bloch equations are considered briefly in Appendix D.)

Now, the *line-width* of the n.m.r. signal is determined by the lifetime of the particular spin-state (because of the Heisenberg Uncertainty Principle) and this can be expressed as $\delta\omega \simeq 1/\delta t$. (Note that $\delta\omega = 2\pi\delta\nu$.) For an unsaturated signal, this lifetime δt is equal to the spin–spin relaxation time T_2, and so a narrow line is associated with a long T_2. For many liquids T_1 and T_2 are several seconds (the relaxation is very inefficient), and so the n.m.r. lines are very narrow. Chemical exchange tends to broaden the resonance lines because it reduces T_2.

The effect of chemical exchange on T_1 and T_2

Suppose that there are two protons in environments A and B in the system under investigation, and that they have resonances at frequencies ω_A and ω_B respectively, with no spin coupling between them. If there is no chemical exchange between them or with another species, or if the rate of such exchange is low compared to $1/T_1$ and $1/T_2$, then two sharp lines are observed corresponding to the Larmor frequencies of the protons in the two environments (Figure 2.19(*a*)) and no kinetic information can be obtained.

If the exchange rate is increased, the two lines tend to broaden and approach each other, and eventually to coalesce and sharpen (Figure 2.19(*b*)–(*f*)). This is a reflection of the fact that the transfer of the observed nucleus from A to B is, in effect, a contribution to its relaxation in site A, proportional to its rate of transfer, $1/\tau_A$. Correspondingly, its transfer from B to A contributes $1/\tau_B$ to its relaxation at B. (This assumes that the exchange of nuclei between A and B takes place in a time which is very short compared to the relaxation time of the nuclei when actually present at the sites—i.e. that no change of magnetization occurs during the transfer.) If the exchange process involves one site which is being observed and one which is not, a similar situation obtains. We can see that the spin–lattice and spin–spin relaxation rates of the nuclei in sites A and B are going to be modified by the terms $1/\tau_A$ and $1/\tau_B$, respectively. Thus the total spin–lattice relaxation rates become $1/T'_{1A} = 1/T_{1A} + 1/\tau_A$ and

$1/T'_{1B} = 1/T_{1B} + 1/\tau_B$ where T'_{1A}, T'_{1B} are the times in the presence of exchange and T_{1A}, T_{1B} are the times in the absence of exchange. Similarly $1/T'_{2A} = 1/T_{2A} + 1/\tau_A$ and $1/T'_{2B} = 1/T_{2B} + 1/\tau_B$. These terms are substituted into the Bloch equations which can, in principle, be solved (see Appendix D). The expressions are rather complicated, however, and various simplifications can be made in the regions of slow, fast and intermediate

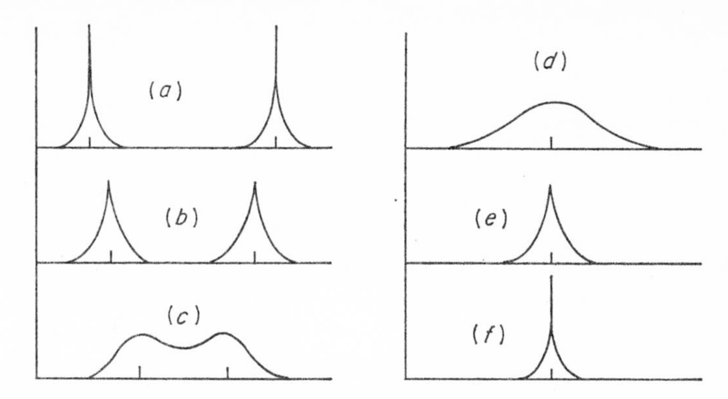

FIGURE 2.19 Schematic representation of the n.m.r. spectra of two exchanging nuclei. (*a*)–(*f*) represents increasing exchange rate. (The ordinates are not to the same scale.)

exchange. In particular, it is usually sufficient just to consider the spin–spin relaxation rate $1/T_2$ which is frequently measured from the line-width.

(i) *Slow exchange.* If there are still two completely separated lines the broadening can be treated very simply. Provided that saturation has not occurred we can write $\delta\nu_A = 1/\pi(1/T_{2A} + 1/\tau_A)$ and $\delta\nu_B = 1/\pi(1/T_{2B} + 1/\tau_B)$ and solve for $1/\tau_A$ and $1/\tau_B$ by subtracting the respective line-widths $[=1/(\pi T_{2A})$ and $1/(\pi T_{2B})]$ in the absence of exchange. $\delta\nu_A$ and $\delta\nu_B$ are the line-widths at half their maximum height. In the case that the intensities of the lines are not equal, we can use the relations $\tau_A/\tau_B = x_A/x_B = k_B/k_A$ where x_A, x_B are the mole fractions and k_A, k_B the rate constants $(=1/\tau_A$, $1/\tau_B)$. The weaker signal will be the more broadened. The condition for the application of this method is that τ_A and τ_B should be large compared with $|\omega_A - \omega_B|^{-1}$, and evidently the larger the separation between the two signals the greater the rate which can be measured in this way with reasonable accuracy. If one of the species involved in the exchange does not have an observable peak but the other one does, the rate of exchange with respect to the latter can still be obtained since it is not necessary to know the number or nature of the other sites to be able to estimate the rate of disappearance from an observable site.

(ii) *Fast exchange.* If τ_A and τ_B are small compared with $|\omega_A - \omega_B|^{-1}$ we find that the two lines become coalesced (Figure 2.19(*d*)–(*f*)). As the exchange rate increases the situation is reached (Figure 2.19(*f*)) at which, no matter how fast the exchange becomes, the single resonance line is narrowed no further. This marks the upper boundary of rates which can be measured by the method. The completely coalesced line is centred at an average frequency $\nu = x_A\nu_A + x_B\nu_B$ and is characterized by an averaged spin–spin relaxation time $1/T_2' = x_A/T_{2A} + x_B/T_{2B}$. If the exchange process is slow enough to contribute to the signal width but is still much faster than that corresponding to separated signals we can use the approximation $1/T_2'' = 1/T_2' + x_A^2x_B^2(\omega_A - \omega_B)^2(\tau_A + \tau_B)$. The sum $(\tau_A + \tau_B)$ can therefore be determined from the excess broadening compared with the completely coalesced line.

(iii) *Intermediate exchange.* The region in which τ_A and τ_B are comparable with $|\omega_A - \omega_B|^{-1}$ is the most difficult to analyse quantitatively. At the coalescence point the exchange broadening is generally greatest and, despite the fact that it is not usually very sharply defined, the temperature at which this occurs is sometimes used to estimate τ. Another way of determining τ in this region is the so-called intensity ratio method. The two lines are assumed to have Lorentzian shape (see Appendix D) and an expression is used which relates τ and the ratio of intensities at the peak and at the valley midway between the peaks.[26]

To summarize, we measure rates of reaction by the effect of the chemical exchange on T_1 and T_2. This may be determined by computing the line-width from the full modified Bloch equations although it is sometimes possible to use certain approximations. (It is also possible to determine T_1 and T_2 directly and methods for doing this will be considered at the end of this section.) From this analysis we obtain the lifetime τ and we use this to evaluate the various rate constants. For example, in a reaction involving A, B, . . . with kinetic orders $a, b, \ldots$, dc_A/dt is given by

$$\frac{dc_A}{dt} = kc_A^a c_B^b \ldots = \frac{c_A}{\tau_A}$$

A pseudo first-order rate constant (τ_A^{-1}) is measured in every case. In order to evaluate $a, b, \ldots$, τ_A is measured as a function of the concentrations of A, B, ... It will be apparent that the limitations on the rates which can be measured by n.m.r. are fairly severe because τ must be comparable to T_2 and $|\omega_A - \omega_B|^{-1}$. However, since many reactions involving resonating species, especially ^1H, are second order, it is often possible to adjust the concentrations so that the overall (first-order) rate constant falls within the required range.

We shall now discuss three systems in which the n.m.r. method has been used. The first system is chemically very simple and involves conformational changes in an organic molecule. The second is rather more complex in that it involves the transfer of a proton between two species. The third system involves the transfer of a solvent molecule from the inner coordination sphere of a paramagnetic metal ion to the bulk solvent.

The kinetics of conformational change

At room temperature the spectrum of the *N*-methyl groups of *NN*-dimethylacetamide is a doublet (cf. Figure 2.19(*a*)) because the mesomerism (2.6) imparts a certain amount of double-bond character to the central CN bond. Although the *N*-methyl protons are equivalent in form II they are non-equivalent in form III, being either *cis* or *trans* to the carbonyl

$$\mathrm{MeC(=O)N(Me)_2}\ \text{(II)} \quad \leftrightarrow \quad \mathrm{Me(^{-}O)C{=}N^{+}(Me)_2}\ \text{(III)} \qquad (2.6)$$

group. As the temperature is raised the rate of rotation around the central CN bond increases until it is comparable to $\Delta\omega$. The lines broaden and coalesce to a single line which becomes sharper on further heating, as illustrated in Figure 2.19.

Gutowsky and Holm,[27] who were the first to analyse this system, modified the Bloch equations to take into account the conformational change involving the two isomers of form III. They considered the system as one in which there are two sites with different local fields giving a resonance with two components A and B. The relative intensities of the two components are directly proportional to the proton fractions p_A and p_B contributing to them. Since the two sites are energetically equivalent, they will be occupied equally and $p_A = p_B = \frac{1}{2}$. The average lifetime of the proton at the two sites is therefore $\tau = \frac{1}{2}k$ where k is the zero-order rate constant for the conformational change. Gutowsky and Holm determined values of τ from the line shape at different temperatures. The temperature dependence of k is given by $k = A \exp(-E_A/RT)$ where A is the frequency factor and E_A the potential energy barrier hindering the internal rotation so, by plotting $\log(\tau\delta\omega)$ against $1/T$, they were able to estimate E_A. They obtained a value of 12 ± 2 kcal/mole, although it is fair to point out that others have used different n.m.r. techniques to measure this quantity in the analogue, *NN*-dimethylformamide (DMF), and have obtained values varying from 7 to 24 kcal/mole. The reason for this wide discrepancy and, indeed, the correct value for the barrier to internal rotation in DMF are still not known, despite the fact that this has been one of the most extensively studied processes by the n.m.r. method. Perhaps this result should be taken as a warning that, although these methods are very powerful, the finer details of their application to chemical kinetics have not yet been completely evaluated. There seem to be systematic errors associated with the different techniques and the reader is referred to a very good critical discussion of this point.[28]

A similar problem which has been solved by n.m.r. concerns the rate of inversion of cyclohexane. Cyclohexane exists as a rapidly exchanging mixture of degenerate chair forms, represented by equation (2.7). The

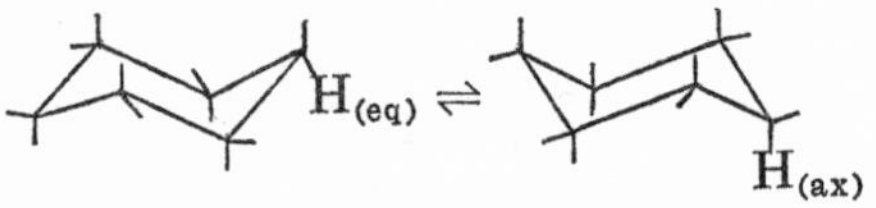

$$H_{(eq)} \rightleftharpoons H_{(ax)} \tag{2.7}$$

protons in the equatorial position resonate at a rather lower field than those in the axial position so, if reaction (2.7) takes place in a time which is long compared with the reciprocal chemical shift, we shall expect to see two signals corresponding to a particular proton. In fact, the spectrum of cyclohexane is highly complex and the situation is simplified considerably if all of the H atoms except one are replaced by D. At room temperature the reaction is rapid and a single narrow line is observed. As the temperature is lowered the residence time in each chair conformation becomes comparable to $\Delta\omega^{-1}$ and the peak separates into two equalized peaks. Anet and Bourn[29] used line-shape analysis and double resonance to evaluate the rate constants and activation parameters for reaction (2.7) ($\Delta H^{\ddagger} = 10{\cdot}8$ kcal/mole). Since it is very likely that a boat or twist boat is an intermediate in the chair–chair interconversion, they have concluded that the observed rate constant $k = \frac{1}{2}k_{cb}$, where k_{cb} is the rate constant for the chair–boat or chair–twist boat process. The factor $\frac{1}{2}$ enters because, out of the molecules which become boats, half will revert to their initial chair form and the other half will go over into the inverted chair form.

Although the n.m.r. method has been applied to several conformational changes of this type,[30] there are two important difficulties which hamper work on ring inversions. In the first place the spectra are very complex and it is not correct to apply the theory derived for the collapse of a doublet. In the second place the barriers to inversion are often rather low and it is necessary to work at low temperatures in order to slow down the inversion process sufficiently.

Intermolecular proton-transfer

So far, we have been dealing with systems in which spin–spin coupling can be neglected. In fact, the collapse of a spin multiplet can sometimes be very valuable in measuring rates of exchange of magnetic nuclei. A considerable amount of work has been done on proton exchange in

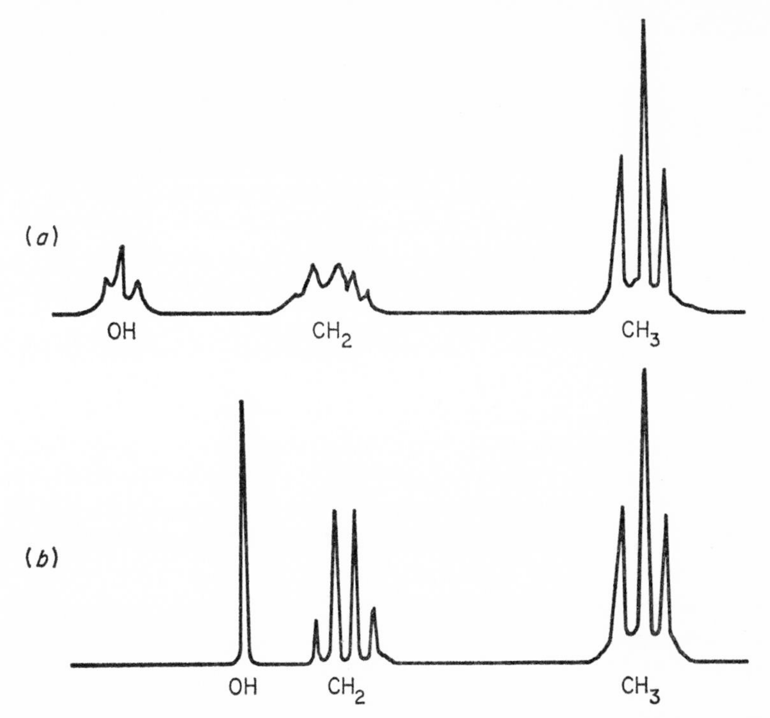

FIGURE 2.20 N.m.r. spectra of (*a*) pure, dry ethanol, and (*b*) ethanol to which a little CCl_4 has been added.

alcohols and amines and we shall consider one of the simplest of these systems, proton exchange in ethanol.

The spectrum of pure dry ethanol is shown in Figure 2.20(*a*). If a little water is added, an extra line due to the H_2O-proton appears between the OH- and CH_2-bands. As the concentration of water increases three things happen. The OH triplet of ethanol sharpens to a singlet, this then broadens and coalesces with the H_2O band, and at the same time the CH_2 signal becomes a simple quadruplet. These are all consistent with an increasing rate of proton exchange between the OH groups of ethanol and the various species present in water (e.g. OH^-, H_2O), and it is possible to determine the exchange lifetime from the temperature dependence of the coalescence.

The addition of a small amount of HCl or NaOH to pure ethanol also leads to a sharpening of the hydroxyl peak and the corresponding simplification of the methylene band (cf. Figure 2.20(*b*)). Again, exchange of the OH proton is the cause but this time several reactions of the type,

$$\text{EtOH} + \text{A} \rightleftharpoons \text{EtO}^- + \text{AH}^+$$

are involved. It is possible[31] to evaluate the rate constants for these exchange reactions by comparing the shape of the CH_2-band with the theoretical curves.

A third interesting observation is that in pure dry ethanol the chemical shift of the hydroxyl proton relative to the methylene group decreases as the temperature is raised. This has been explained in the following way. In ethanol it is known that the hydroxyl protons are involved in hydrogen-bonding to the oxygen atoms of other ethanol molecules and we should expect that a hydrogen atom which is involved in H-bonding would be subject to a different degree of magnetic shielding compared with one which is not. If the exchange between the two sites is fast, the proton resonance corresponds to the weighted average shielding for the two sites. As the temperature is altered, the proportion of ethanol molecules which are hydrogen-bonded will also change and so will the weighting factors. This will mean that the resonance frequency of the OH proton will be temperature-dependent. This explanation is confirmed by the observation of a similar effect when a non-hydrogen-bonding solvent such as carbon tetrachloride is added (Figure 2.20(*b*)). Many similar *hydrogen-bond shifts* have been observed, and it is sometimes possible to measure the lifetime of the H-bonded state, or at least to estimate its upper limit.[32]

Solvent exchange at a paramagnetic ion

If we dissolve a paramagnetic metal ion M^{2+} in a proton-containing solvent we expect to observe two sets of peaks: one due to the bulk solvent, as before, and another downfield due to the solvent in the inner coordination sphere of the metal (Chapter 3). The latter is shifted because of the large magnetic field in the immediate neighbourhood of M^{2+}. In addition, the interaction of the unpaired electrons of the paramagnetic ion results in rapid nuclear relaxation, both dipole–dipole and scalar hyperfine interactions contributing. We thus have the solvent protons in two chemically different environments with the possibility of measuring the rate of exchange between the two. It is possible to obtain rate constants from a consideration of $|\omega_A - \omega_B|$, as above, but it often happens that the line due to the solvent in the neighbourhood of the metal ion is very weak and broad and this makes it difficult to measure $|\omega_A - \omega_B|$ precisely. The rate constants for exchange can still be obtained from measurements of T_1 and T_2 from the signal of the bulk solvent and in this section we shall concentrate on this method.

What can cause relaxation of a proton in a molecule in the bulk of the solvent? The mechanism can be the same as when there is no M^{2+}, through tumbling etc., but it is always found that another process reduces T_1 and T_2, namely the long-range interaction between the bulk protons outside the first coordination sphere and the metal ion. This is often called *second-sphere broadening* and the detailed mechanism is unimportant for our purposes. It is known to occur quite independently of any exchange between the first coordination sphere and the bulk since it is observed in solutions of the non-labile paramagnetic species Cr (III). When exchange is possible, however, and if the molecules of the bulk solvent are able to exchange with those at the ion in a time less than T_{2b} (i.e. $\tau_b \ll T_{2b}$), several other forms of relaxation become feasible and the situation becomes much more interesting. [Throughout this section we shall use T_{2b} and T_{2M} to represent the spin–spin (transverse) relaxation times of the proton in the bulk solvent and in the first coordination sphere, respectively, and τ_b, τ_M to represent the corresponding lifetimes of the solvent molecule.] If the solvent remains coordinated long enough for relaxation to occur (i.e. $\tau_M \gg T_{2M}$), the proton will be relaxed every time the molecule enters that environment. (Even if it is not kept for so long in the paramagnetic environment, relaxation can sometimes occur.) Thus, a solvent molecule spends most of its time in the bulk phase, but will occasionally bind to the metal for a brief period. During this time the relaxation occurs since coordination to the metal effectively produces a paramagnetic pulse which alters the phase of the precessing nucleus.

The Bloch equations were modified first for this situation by Swift and Connick.[33] They obtained an expression for the difference between the line-width of the *bulk* solvent in the presence $(1/T_{2b})$ and the absence $(1/T_{2a})$ of the metal ion:

$$\frac{1}{T_{2p}} = \left(\frac{1}{T_{2b}} - \frac{1}{T_{2a}}\right) = \left(\frac{p_M}{\tau_b \tau_M}\right) \left[\frac{1/T_{2M}^2 + 1/(T_{2M}\tau_M) + \Delta\omega_M^2}{(1/T_{2M} + 1/\tau_M)^2 + \Delta\omega_M^2}\right] \qquad (2.8)$$

where p_M is a statistical factor which represents the number of solvent molecules in the inner coordination sphere (the lifetimes of the solvent in the bulk and inner sphere are related by the expression $1/\tau_b = p_M/\tau_M$) and $\Delta\omega_M$ is the shift in Larmor frequencies in the two environments (i.e. the chemical shift). They took the limiting cases in which each of the four squared rate terms in equation (2.8) is larger than the others and therefore contributes the major part to $1/T_{2p}$.

(a) $\Delta\omega_M^2 \gg 1/T_{2M}^2, 1/\tau_M^2$. This is called the '$\Delta\omega$ mechanism' of relaxation. Relaxation occurs merely through the change in the precessional frequency of the nucleus in the two environments, as explained above. Substitution gives $1/T_{2p} = p_M/\tau_M = 1/\tau_b$ and it can be seen that $1/T_{2p}$ is controlled by the rate of chemical exchange.

(b) $1/\tau_M^2 \gg \Delta\omega_M^2 \gg 1/(T_{2M}\tau_M)$. As in (a) the relaxation occurs through a change in the precessional frequency but here the *rate* of this change is limiting since the chemical exchange rate is high. Substitution gives $1/T_{2p} = p_M\tau_M\Delta\omega_M^2$ and the line-width contribution of the paramagnetic ion is still dependent on the chemical exchange rate.

(c) $1/T_{2M}^2 \gg \Delta\omega_M^2, 1/\tau_M^2$, i.e. relaxation by T_{2M} is fast. Again, $1/T_{2p}$ is controlled by the rate of chemical exchange since substitution gives $1/T_{2p} = p_M/\tau_M = 1/\tau_b$.

(d) $1/(T_{2M}\tau_M) \gg 1/T_{2M}^2, \Delta\omega_M^2$, i.e. chemical exchange is still fast but $1/T_{2M}$ and $\Delta\omega_M$ are comparable to each other. This gives $1/T_{2p} = p_M/T_{2M}$ and indicates that the broadening is not now controlled by chemical exchange but by the T_{2M} relaxation process.

Let us now consider a particular case, the variation of $1/T_{2p}$ with temperature for the system Ni^{2+} in acetonitrile. The variation with temperature provides an excellent way of seeing which range we are in, since the different limiting processes have different activation energies. Swift and Connick actually studied ^{17}O resonance in enriched water and measured the water exchange rates at various metal ions, though the approach is applicable to any suitable nucleus in any solvent. In fact, acetonitrile, methanol, etc., are in some ways better solvents in that wider temperature ranges can be covered.

At low temperatures the solvent exchange is so slow that none of the mechanisms (a)–(d) above is applicable (i.e. we are in the region of slow exchange, p. 53) and we get only second-sphere broadening (Region I of Figure 2.21(*a*)). We can therefore obtain no information about the rate of of the solvent exchange process. It has actually been shown that in several these systems the dipole–dipole interaction mechanism is dominant and the hyperfine interaction contributes only a few per cent to the relaxation. The decrease of $1/T_{2p}$ with decreasing reciprocal temperature corresponds to an apparent activation energy of the electron relaxation process (which is what determines the correlation time of this dipole–dipole interaction) of about 1 kcal/mole.

As the sample is heated the exchange becomes important and we enter region II (the intermediate region of p. 54). In this region mechanisms (a) or (c) are operative since the exchange rate $1/\tau_M$ is much less than either the chemical shift $\Delta\omega_M$ or the relaxation rate at the metal $1/T_{2M}$. Hence $1/T_{2p} = 1/\tau_b$ and so the slope of the plot of log $(1/T_{2p})$ against $1/T$ gives a

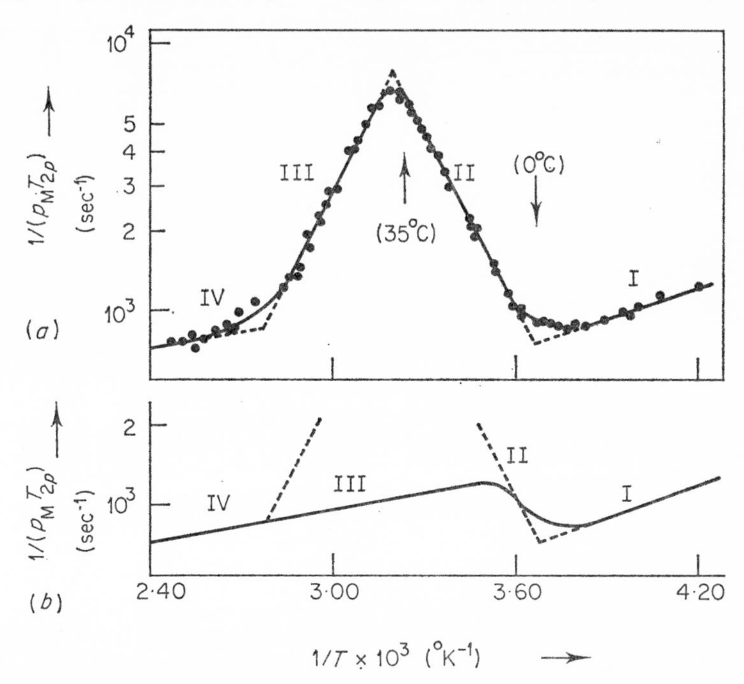

FIGURE 2.21 Temperature dependence for the protons in CH_3CN solutions of $Ni(CH_3CN)_6^{2+}$ at 56·4 MHz of (*a*) $1/(p_M T_{2p})$ [data from D. K. Ravage, T. R. Stengle and C. H. Langford, *Inorg. Chem.*, **6**, 1252 (1967)], and (*b*) $1/(p_M T_{1p})$ (see text).

direct measurement of the activation energy for the exchange of solvent at the metal ion. For acetonitrile at nickel this is 13·9 kcal/mole.

As the solution is heated further, τ_M decreases further and we reach region III where, although it is still intermediate (cf. p. 54), the rate of exchange $1/\tau_M$ is now greater than the shift. This corresponds to mechanism (b). Since the line-width broadening now depends linearly on τ_M, it will change rapidly with temperature, but in the opposite sense from region II. If the chemical shift $\Delta\omega_M$ is independently known, the exchange rate can be determined. The maximum broadening of the lines corresponds to an exchange rate equal to $\Delta\omega_M$ and occurs in the borderline between regions II and III.

Finally, in region IV the exchange is so rapid that it no longer affects the line-width (mechanism (d)). The process is a non-chemical one and so its activation energy is small, as in region I.

The variation of T_1 with temperature is shown in Figure 2.21(*b*) and it will be seen that the exchange process has an effect on it as well as T_2 in region II, although it is somewhat less. Because its regions III and IV are effectively combined, T_1 is much less useful for determining solvent exchange rates than T_2. Qualitatively, the earlier levelling out of T_1 may be understood quite simply. The chemical exchange process is only important in determining the spin–lattice relaxation time in the region where $1/\tau_M \approx \Delta\omega_M$; much above or below this value, other factors determine T_1. Use of this fact is made in measuring the 'enhancement of proton relaxation rate' ε, which is a function of $1/T_1$ in the presence and absence of, for example, some macromolecule. This property has been used by Cohn, especially for investigating the binding of Mn^{2+} to proteins and the subsequent binding of a substrate at the bound metal.[34] Since ε is a static rather than a kinetic factor it would evidently be inconvenient if the chemical exchange rate affected it.

To summarize, we can obtain some information about the kinetics of solvent exchange from regions II and III (T_2) or II (T_1). The results which have been obtained this way are consistent with those obtained from chemical-shift data.

Measurement of T_1 and T_2

We have seen that the most common way of measuring the lifetime of an exchanging species has been through an analysis of the line shapes. This technique requires the normal high-resolution n.m.r. spectrometer and the spectrum is swept through in slow passage condition. The field $\mathbf{H}_0$ is altered sufficiently slowly that the distribution of the magnetic species among the available energy levels is able to keep pace. Although the method is conceptually simple it is sometimes very difficult to solve the Bloch equations rigorously and various approximations are often made. For example, the line-width of the nucleus undergoing chemical exchange ($1/T_2'$) has a non-exchange contribution ($1/T_{2,0}$) and an exchange contribution ($1/T_{2,e}$). $1/T_{2,0}$ is usually determined by local inhomogeneities in the magnetic field and a measure of it can be obtained by including in the sample tube a reference compound whose signal width is taken as that corresponding to the non-exchange contribution. Thus, the lifetime of the exchanging nucleus can be calculated from $1/T_{2,e} = 1/T_2' - 1/T_{2,0}$. Another method uses the intensity ratio method (p. 54).

There are, however, several other methods which can be used to determine T_1 and T_2 and these often permit the range of rates which can be measured to be extended somewhat, and also produce more accurate data. In the past they have been used primarily by physicists but it seems likely that their use will become more widespread among chemists. We shall consider three methods: fast passage, spin echo and double resonance.

(a) *Fast passage.* If a spectrum is swept through at a rate which is high compared with $1/T_2$ then the nuclei do not have time to reequilibrate between the energy levels as $\mathbf{H}_0$ is changed. This results in a 'ringing' or

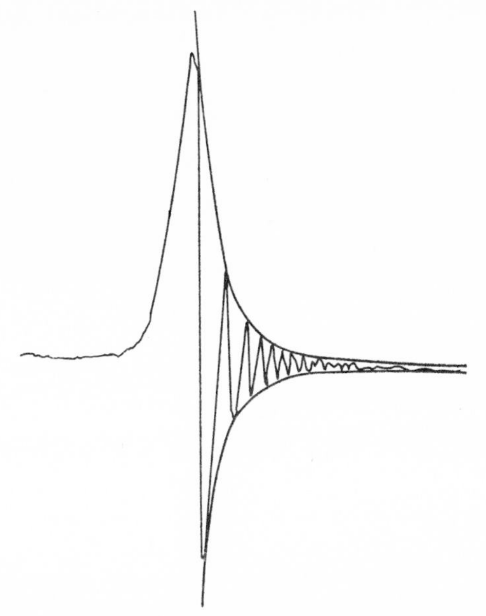

FIGURE 2.22 N.m.r. peak taken under fast passage conditions showing 'ringing'.

'wiggle' signal of the type shown in Figure 2.22. What happens is that the r.f. field is rotating at a frequency which is slightly different from the Larmor frequency at which the nucleus is precessing and so the two beat against each other. The envelope of wiggles depicts the decay of the induced magnetization in the nucleus in the xy plane and is in the form of an exponential with time constant T_2. (The decay depends also on the inhomogeneities in the field and an extended ringing pattern may be used as an indication of proper field adjustment. If the wiggles are caused by field inhomogeneities the method cannot be used to measure T_2.)

(b) *Spin echo.* This is a very ingenious group of methods for determining T_1 and T_2 which uses a steady magnetic field $\mathbf{H}_0$ and short pulses of r.f. field of the resonance frequency H_1. The pulses are of known duration and are applied at known time intervals. Several combinations of pulses have been used and we shall consider the 90°/180° method of Carr and Purcell.[35]

When we switch on the rotating field H_1 it tips the nuclear magnetization vector **M** away from its equilibrium position parallel to the steady field $\mathbf{H}_0$. If H_1 is on for a short period and then switched off again, the direction of **M** is changing by an amount which depends on the length of the pulse. It then precesses about $\mathbf{H}_0$ with the Larmor frequency until the components

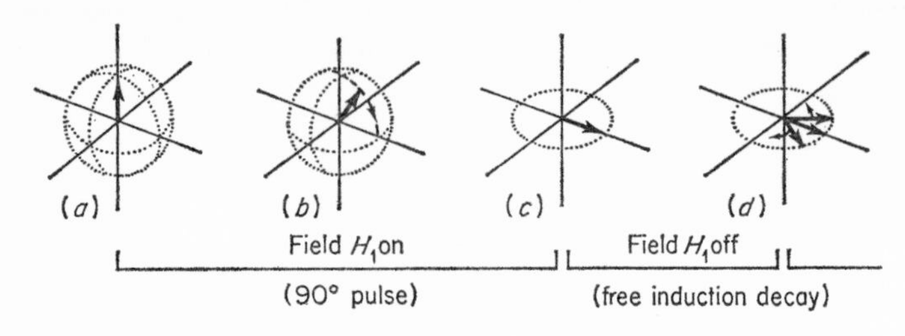

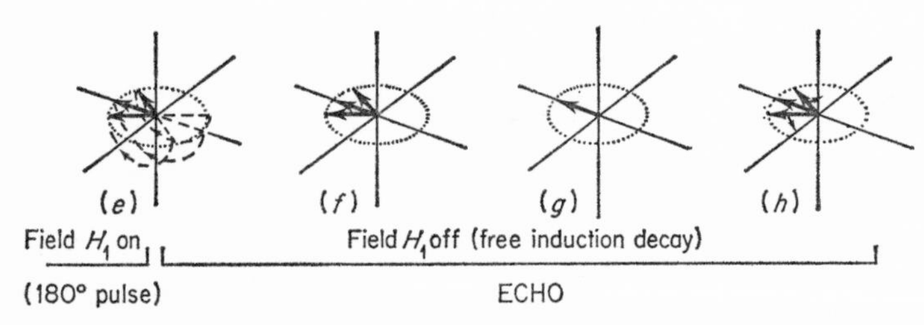

FIGURE 2.23 The formation of a spin echo after successive 90° and 180° pulses (Ref. 35).

in the xy plane have decayed (with relaxation time T_2). The induction signal produced in this period when the r.f. field is off is called *free induction decay*. The rate at which **M** is rotated away from the z direction when H_1 is switched on is given by γH_1 (where γ is the gyromagnetic ratio of the nucleus) and if the duration of the pulse is t_p, then the magnetization vector will be tilted through an angle $\gamma H_1 t_p$. If H_1 and t_p are chosen so that $\gamma H_1 t_p = \pi/2$ the vector is turned into the xy plane. This is called a 90° pulse. Pulses for which $\gamma H_1 t_p = \pi$ are 180° pulses and have the effect of completely reversing the direction of **M**. The amplitude of H_1 is generally fairly large and the duration of the pulse short so that relaxation effects during the on period are as small as possible.

Figure 2.23 illustrates what happens when a 90° pulse and then a 180° pulse are applied. The system is initially in thermal equilibrium with all the spin vectors aligned in the z direction (a) parallel to the static field. The 90° pulse tips the vectors (b) into the rotating $x'y'$ plane (c) and after

H_1 has been switched off free induction decay takes place and the individual vectors fan out in the $x'y'$ plane (*d*). After a known time t_d a 180° pulse is applied which rotates the vectors about the x' axis (*e*). After the second pulse each individual vector continues to move in the $x'y'$ plane in the same direction as before—with the exception that now the fanning motion causes the vectors to close up (*f*). At time $2t_d$ the vectors will be completely reclustered (*g*), leading to a strong resultant moment in the $-y'$ direction. This produces a signal in the detector—the echo. After the echo the vectors again fan out (*h*) and decay in the normal way. The amplitude of the echo is proportional to $\exp(-2t_d/T_2)$, from which T_2 can be evaluated.

Different echo methods have been used for measuring the kinetics of chemical reactions but the results do not always agree with those obtained with high resolution methods. The causes of the discrepancies are not yet understood.[29]

(c) *Double Resonance.* This is another ingenious technique and is essentially a small-perturbation method (cf. section 3). It was first used by Forsén and Hoffman[36] and is applicable where the exchange rate is comparable to $1/T_1$.

Suppose we have a system in which a magnetic nucleus is exchanging between two non-equivalent sites A and B. If we strongly irradiate the sample with signal B, and thereby disturb the spin populations at site B,

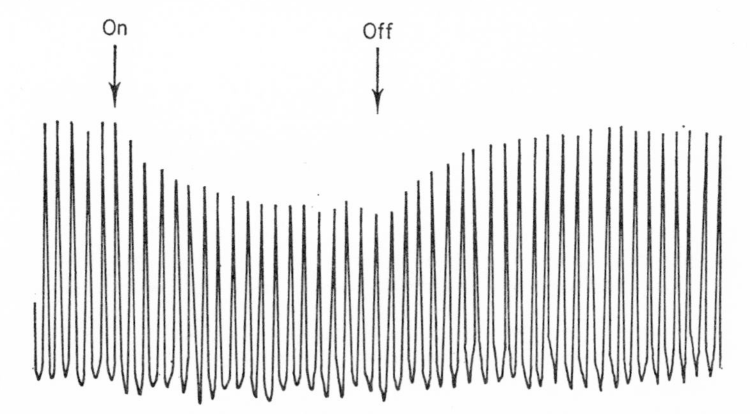

FIGURE 2.24 Double Resonance method. Arrows indicate application and removal of B resonance signal (Ref. 36).

we find that the disturbance is also experienced at site A, provided that T_{1A} is not much shorter than the exchange time. Hence, if we are looking at the signal produced by the nucleus at site A and then suddenly irradiate with the r.f. field appropriate to site B, we shall expect to see the signal decay to a new equilibrium value, and then grow to its original intensity when the irradiation of B is stopped (Figure 2.24). The decay of the z-component of the magnetization at A, M_{zA}, is given by equation (2.9)

$$M_{zA}(t) = M_{0A}\left(\frac{\tau_{1A}}{\tau_A}\,e^{-t/\tau_{1A}} + \frac{\tau_{1A}}{T_{1A}}\right) \tag{2.9}$$

where M_{0A} is the normal magnetization at A, $1/\tau_{1A} = 1/\tau_A + 1/T_{1A}$, and the other symbols have their usual meanings. From the semilogarithmic plot of the exponential it is possible to obtain τ_{1A} and, from the initial and final equilibrium intensities, τ_{1A}/T_{1A}. Thus, from a single experiment both τ_A and T_{1A} can be determined. By monitoring signal B and irradiating with signal A it is likewise possible to determine τ_B and T_{1B}. No complications arise if the populations of sites A and B are unequal.

(b) Electron paramagnetic resonance and other absorption methods

In the same way that certain nuclei possess spin and associated magnetic moments, an unpaired electron has a spin and a corresponding magnetic moment. As with the proton, the electron can exhibit spins of $\pm\frac{1}{2}$ and when a steady magnetic field is applied it may take up only one of two positions. It may be made to pass between the two states by the application of an oscillating electromagnetic field perpendicular to the steady field and the experimental arrangement is rather similar to that used with n.m.r. in that the steady magnetic field corresponding to the resonance condition is determined for an oscillating field of fixed frequency. In the case of e.p.r. the resonance occurs in the microwave region when $\mathbf{H}_0$ is of the order of 10^4 gauss. The reason for the higher frequency is the much larger magnetic moment of the electron compared with that of a nucleus, such as the proton. Generally, the unpaired electron interacts with species of finite nuclear spin, such as ^1H and ^{14}N, with the result that the absorption has a hyperfine structure. This has the advantage that it is usually possible to identify with certainty the radical under investigation. As with n.m.r., it is possible to describe the shape of an e.p.r. line mathematically and the lifetime of the radical can be determined from the broadening at half height.

Let us consider a system which has been studied this way. The negative ion of naphthalene can be made in a suitable solvent, such as dimethoxyethane (DME) by treatment with an alkali metal in the absence of oxygen. This stable radical-ion has an e.p.r. spectrum with hyperfine structure and, if more naphthalene is added, a broadening of the spectral lines occurs which is attributed to reaction (2.10),

$$\text{(naphthalene)}^- + \text{(naphthalene)} \rightleftharpoons \text{(naphthalene)} + \text{(naphthalene)}^-$$

$$[N^- + N \rightleftharpoons N + N^-] \tag{2.10}$$

This is a second-order reaction with rate constant k and it may be shown[37] that $c_{N^-}/\tau_{N^-} = c_N/\tau_N = kc_Nc_{N^-}$ (as for the n.m.r. treatment), so that $k = 1/c_N\tau_{N^-}$. This may be expressed in terms of the line-width at half height, but it is much simpler experimentally to measure the difference in field between the extremities of the first-derivative spectrum. This difference ΔH_M is the difference in the fields corresponding to maximum positive and negative slopes of the Lorentzian absorption curve. k is then given by $1{\cdot}6 \times 10^7\ \Delta H_M/c_N$, where the numerical constant contains the Landé g-factor, the Bohr magneton and Planck's constant.

This is one of several reactions of this type in which an organic negative radical-ion and its parent molecule react in the presence of an alkali metal. It has been found that the rate constants depend on the nature of the metal and to account for this it has been postulated that the metal is involved in a bridging role in the activated complex, e.g. dipy . . . K^+ . . . dipy$^-$ for the case of 2,2′-dipyridyl (dipy). In the case of benzophenone with sodium in DME, the spectrum of the radical-ion has many hyperfine lines arising through the interaction of the free electron with ^1H and ^{23}Na nuclei. When benzophenone is added, the structure due to the proton interaction disappears and only the lines associated with the sodium interaction remain. To account for this, it is suggested[38] that the unpaired electron moves rapidly over all the proton positions (too fast for the lines characteristic of the electron in the different proton environments to be seen), but relatively slowly from one sodium nucleus to the other. In other words, the transfer of an electron from one molecule to another is associated with the transfer of the cation.

Electron paramagnetic resonance has also been used in conjunction with flow methods for studying radical reactions in the gas phase and in solution, but there is no difference of principle compared with the use of, for example, visible absorption (see section 1).

There have been recent investigations in which Raman line broadening has been used for studying reaction rates.[39] For example, the 1435 cm^{-1} band of the trifluoroacetate ion CF_3COO^- is broadened considerably in acid as compared with neutral solution. This may be because its lifetime is shortened on account of the reaction $H^+ + CF_3COO^- \rightleftharpoons CF_3COOH$. The broadening of other spectral bands, such as electronic spectra in solution,[40] has also been discussed in terms of the mean lifetimes of the excited state of the molecule.

(c) Fluorescence quenching

In this method the chemical reaction competes with the fluorescence of one of the reactants. The absorption of light of low wavelength by a solution of a species A may produce excited molecules $\overset{*}{A}$ which return to their ground state through the emission of fluorescence. If the illumination is continuous and of constant intensity, a steady state will be set up in which the rate of formation of $\overset{*}{A}$ is balanced by the rate of its deactivation (as in n.m.r.) and the intensity of fluorescence is proportional to the steady-state concentration of $\overset{*}{A}$. The upper rate limit of reactions which can be studied this way is determined by the time taken for the molecule to become excited, which is about 10^{-12} sec, and the lower limit is determined by the lifetime of the fluorescing species, which is generally of the order of 10^{-8} sec. In view of the requirement that one species fluoresce and the restriction on the half-lives of the subsequent reaction, this is not one of the most generally useful of the fast reaction methods. However, it has yielded some interesting results and we shall consider its application in a little more detail.

In order to determine the rate of a chemical reaction by this method it is necessary to measure the relative fluorescence intensities in the presence of known concentrations of a quenching agent (species B) and also the mean lifetime of the fluorescing molecule $\overset{*}{A}$ in the absence of B. The first of these is easily done in a commercial spectrofluorimeter but the latter is more difficult since it is typically 10^{-9} to 10^{-7} sec and the ordinary oscilloscope cannot sweep sufficiently fast to present the fluorescence decay curve directly. The method commonly used is to measure the phase shift $\Delta\phi$ between a sinusoidally modulated light source and the resultant fluorescence, which has the same period as the light source. The applied frequency ν is usually about 10^7 Hz, and the lifetime τ_0 is given by the equation $\tau_0 = \tan \Delta\phi/2\pi\nu$. It is possible to modulate the light source to such a frequency by passing it through a liquid across which a periodic disturbance is applied, such as ultrasonic waves (the Debye–Sears effect, see p. 45).

Before the energy can be transferred from $\overset{*}{A}$ to B the two species must form an encounter complex in which their solvent cages have been sufficiently modified to allow significant chemical interaction, and we can consider two distinct mechanisms for this quenching process involving B. In the dynamic, or diffusional, mechanism the excited state $\overset{*}{A}$ is formed in comparative isolation from B and the encounter complex is produced in the second step:

$$A(+B) \xrightarrow{h\nu} \overset{*}{A} + B \longrightarrow \overset{*}{A}\,.\,B \xrightarrow{k} \text{products}$$

In the static pathway the molecule of A which is excited is already in close proximity to B:

$$A + B \rightleftharpoons A\,.\,B \xrightarrow{h\nu} \overset{*}{A}\,.\,B \xrightarrow{k} \text{products}$$

Now, in the absence of B, $\overset{*}{A}$ may lose its energy either by the emission of fluorescence or by some non-radiative process such as interaction with the solvent and we can represent the rate constants or probabilities for these two processes by n_f and n_d respectively.[41] The lifetime of the excited state is then $(n_f + n_d)^{-1}$ sec and the quantum yield ϕ_0 of the fluorescence process is $n_f/(n_f + n_d) = n_f\tau_0$ where τ_0 is the lifetime of $\overset{*}{A}$ in the absence of B. When B is present a third method of energy dissipation from $\overset{*}{A}$ is by chemical reaction. If the concentration of B (c_B) is much larger than that of $\overset{*}{A}$, which it usually is, the pseudo-first-order rate constant for this reaction is kc_B. The lifetime of $\overset{*}{A}$ is now given by $\tau = (n_f + n_d + kc_B)^{-1}$ sec and the quantum yield is $\phi = n_f/(n_f + n_d + kc_B) = \phi_0/(1 + kc_B\tau_0)$. The ratio of the quantum yields, which is equal to the ratio of the measured fluorescence intensities in the presence and absence of B, is therefore given by $\phi/\phi_0 = (1 + kc_B\tau_0)^{-1}$ and the rate constant can be determined from the variation of ϕ/ϕ_0 with c_B provided that τ_0 is known. This is the Stern–Volmer equation.

In one important respect this derivation is not complete. In the same way that there are two pathways for the formation of the encounter complex $\overset{*}{A}$. B, there are two ways in which it can react. Because the average reaction time is comparable to the time taken for the steady-state to be established, only a certain fraction w of the excited molecules will obey the Stern–Volmer equation. The remaining $(1 - w)$ will react immediately after excitation and so will not contribute to the fluorescence. Thus, if an A molecule has a B molecule within the reaction distance when it is excited, it will react 'immediately' and will therefore not fluoresce. We should predict that the effect of this transient excess reactivity is particularly important the harder it is for $\overset{*}{A}$ and B to diffuse apart, such as when the viscosity of the solvent is high. The relative fluorescence intensities are therefore given more rigorously by $\phi/\phi_0 = w/(1 + kc_B\tau_0)$. The factor w can be calculated from the expression $w = \exp(-V_D c_B)$, where V_D is a characteristic reaction volume surrounding $\overset{*}{A}$ and w represents the probability that no B molecule will be found within this volume. V_D is a function of τ_0, the diffusion coefficients of A and B, and the effective encounter distance. In most cases an approximate value of w is calculated and then, by successive approximations, the rate constant and encounter distance are computed which give the best fit for the data.

In some cases one of the products of the reaction of $\overset{*}{A}$ with B is still excited and can itself fluoresce. This is called 'fluorescence transformation' and, if the spectra of the fluorescing product and $\overset{*}{A}$ are sufficiently different, it can provide some very useful additional information about the reaction. The quantum yield for the species formed by the fluorescence transformation, $\overset{*}{B}$, neglecting the factor w, is given by,

$$\phi' = \phi_0' \left[\frac{kc_B\tau_0}{1 + kc_B\tau_0}\right]$$

If we use the fact that $\phi/\phi_0 + \phi'/\phi_0' = 1$, the plots of fluorescence-intensity ratios against the logarithm of the concentration of B should be symmetrical, as shown in Figure 2.25. If there is an important side reaction

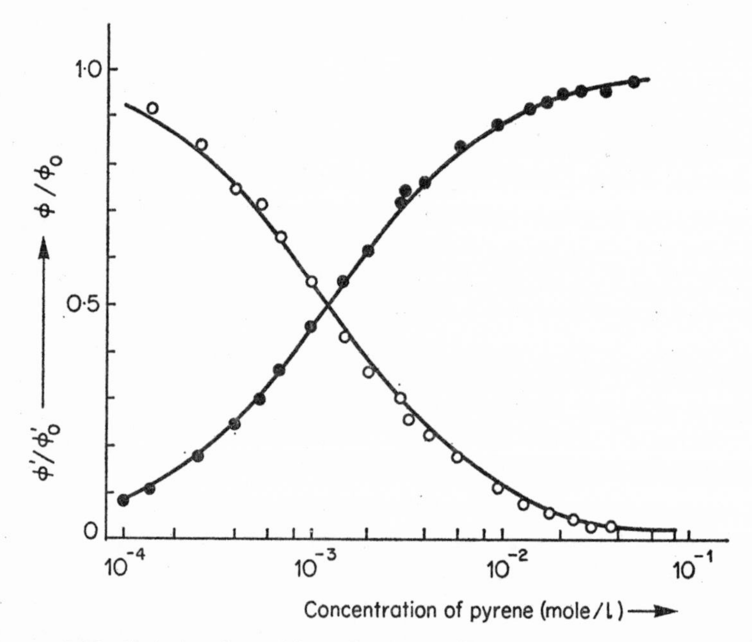

FIGURE 2.25 Relative intensities of pyrene fluorescence in benzene. Open circles represent relative intensity of monomer fluorescence (ϕ/ϕ_0) and filled circles represent relative intensity of dimer fluorescence (ϕ'/ϕ_0'). [E. Döller, Dissertation, Stuttgart, 1960, quoted in Ref. 1, p. 863.]

which has not been considered in the reaction scheme, this will show up in the shape of the plot.

Urban and Weller[42] have measured the fluorescence of certain substituted amino-pyrenes of the type (IV) in various alcohols. In the ground state these amino-pyrenes ($ArNR_2$) are weak acids but in the excited state they are very strong acids, with dissociation constants of the order of 10^2–10^6 mole/l. Thus in strongly acidic media the ground state is mainly in the protonated form $ArNR_2H^+$. Because of restrictions of the Franck–Condon type we would expect the excited form to be $Ar^*Nr_2H^+$, and also that it would have the same molecular environment as the ground state, even though the deprotonated form of the excited state is thermodynamically the more stable. However, the fluorescence spectrum at room temperature was found to correspond to Ar^*NR_2, and this was interpreted by supposing that the deprotonation reaction,

$$Ar^*NR_2H^+ \rightleftharpoons Ar^*NR_2 + H^+ \tag{2.11}$$

is so fast that the lifetime of $Ar^*NR_2H^+$ is much less than its fluorescence lifetime. As the temperature is reduced another emission spectrum appears while the first decreases in intensity. Reaction (2.11) is being slowed down until the deprotonation rate constant becomes comparable with the

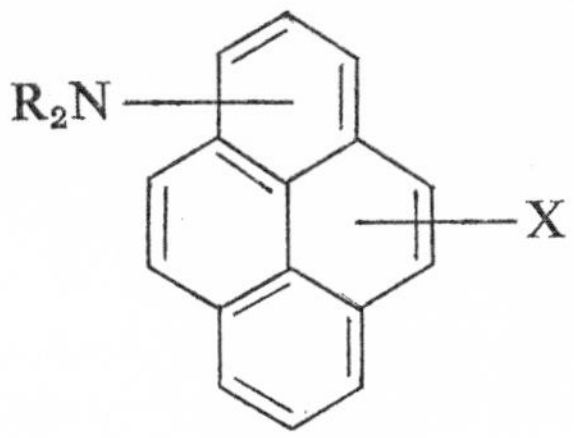

R_2N — X

(IV)

reciprocal fluorescence lifetime of $Ar^*NR_2H^+$, so that eventually no more proton loss occurs and only the fluorescence due to the protonated species is observed. The life times were not actually measured but there is very good reason to suppose that they are of the same order as for unsubstituted pyrene, about 10^{-7} sec. One interesting result of this study is that, although the dissociation constants vary over four orders of magnitude, the dissociation rate constants are independent of the substituents on the ammonium-pyrene but depend significantly on the alcohol used as the solvent. Thus the rate-determining step is independent of factors involving the other groups on $Ar^*NR_2H^+$, such as changes in the solvation of sulphonate groups, but involves the transfer of a proton to the alcohol.

Before leaving the subject of excited molecules it might be pointed out that there is no reason to expect the excited form $\overset{*}{A}$ to exhibit the same reactivity patterns as the ground state A in view of their widely differing energies and electronic wave functions. The differences are usually so large that it is not very fruitful to think of the two as the same species.

(d) Electrochemical methods (polarography)

In the last of the competition methods which we shall discuss, the physical process against which the chemical reaction is competing is diffusion. The electrolytic reduction of a species in a reacting system has different current–voltage characteristics from that of the same species in the absence of a reaction, and these differences can be used to evaluate the reaction rate constants. The conditions which have to be met are fairly stringent: the system must be a good electrical conductor (this has tended to limit the application to aqueous solutions to which large amounts of an inert electrolyte have been added), one of the species must be electrolytically reducible at suitable potentials and the rate constants must fall within certain limits. We shall confine our discussion to one of the more simple electrochemical methods, namely polarography.

In the normal electrolytic reduction process a potential difference is applied between two electrodes placed in the solution and there is a discharge at the cathode of the most easily reduced species $X + e^- \rightarrow A$. (In this section we shall refer to the species which is electroreduced as X. It may be an ion, a molecule or a free radical.) The current flowing is proportional to the rate at which X is reduced and, as we shall see, this can be expressed mathematically in terms of other measurable quantities. The situation is simplified considerably if certain conditions are obeyed. In the first place, the species X must be discharged 'immediately' on arrival at the cathode (the discharge process should not be the rate-limiting step) and in the second place, the cathode should be of a shape whose surface area may be expressed mathematically in simple terms, such as a sphere or an 'infinite' plane. A third simplifying condition is that any ions discharged should not carry the current in the bulk of the solution and this is achieved by using a large excess of an inert electrolyte such as KCl, since the potassium ions are not discharged until most of the species present with less negative electrode potentials have been discharged. The aim is to ensure that the limiting physical process in the electrolysis is the diffusion of X down the concentration gradient between the bulk of the solution and the electrode surface. The current obtained under these conditions is called a *diffusion current*.

Now, suppose that the depolarizer X is involved in a reaction represented by equation (2.12) for which the equilibrium constant is considerably greater than unity.

$$X + B \rightleftharpoons C \tag{2.12}$$

Again, a concentration gradient is set up but, if the dissociation of C into X and B is slower than the electrode process, the discharge of X is controlled partly by diffusion and partly by the backward rate of reaction (2.12). In an extreme case, the overall discharge process may be controlled completely by reaction (2.12) and the corresponding current is known as the *kinetic current*. The kinetic current is less than the diffusion current and it is comparatively easy to distinguish between the two since the former is independent of the head of mercury whereas the latter is not. It is under conditions where the current is kinetically controlled that polarography may be used to determine rate constants.

The apparatus used in polarography is rather simple even though the theory is somewhat difficult to apply. The anode consists of a pool of

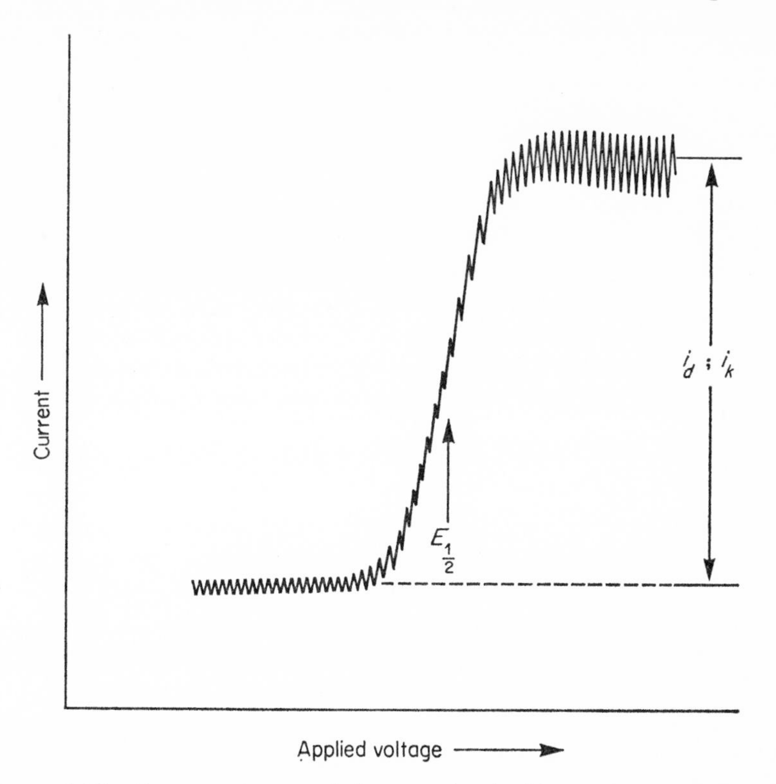

FIGURE 2.26 Current-voltage variation associated with a polarographic wave.

mercury at the bottom of the cell and the dropping-mercury cathode comprises a capillary tube of about 0·03 mm diameter which is connected to a mercury reservoir and held with its tip below the surface of the electrolyte. The mercury head, of the order of 50 cm, is adjusted so as to give a drop every few seconds. A gradually increasing potential difference is applied between the electrodes and the corresponding current is measured. A typical current–voltage plot is shown in Figure 2.26 in which the 'polarographic wave' represents the reduction of X. The half-wave potential $E_{\frac{1}{2}}$ is typical of the species X and the difference between the limiting and residual currents is i_d or i_k. The periodic change in area as each drop grows and falls results in an oscillating current and in practice we can either measure the maximum value i just before the drop falls with a lightly damped instrument or the average current $\bar{\imath}$ with a well-damped instrument. Because the current is only a few microamps, the complete current–voltage curve may be traced several times with the same sample without causing a noticeable change in concentration.

The current is proportional to the rate at which X diffuses to the cathode and it may be represented by the Ilkovič equation. This is usually encountered in the form of equation (2.13),

$$\bar{\imath}_d = 607nD^{\frac{1}{2}}c_X m^{\frac{2}{3}}t_m^{\frac{1}{6}} \tag{2.13}$$

which relates the average diffusion current $\bar{\imath}_d$ to the number of electrons involved in the reduction of one molecule of X, n, the diffusion coefficient of X, D (cm^2/sec), the concentration of X, c_X (m mole/l), the weight of mercury flowing from the capillary in unit time, m (mg/sec) and the drop time, t_m (sec). If the depolarizer takes part in a chemical reaction, the Ilkovič equation is modified in a way which depends on the type of reaction involved. We shall consider the deprotonation of pyruvic acid[43] (reaction (2.14))

$$CH_3COCOOH \underset{k_r}{\overset{k_d}{\rightleftharpoons}} CH_3COCOO^- + H^+ \tag{2.14}$$

In a well-buffered solution the undissociated acid HA is reduced at a more positive potential than (i.e. 'before') the anion A^-. At low pH only one wave, with $E_{\frac{1}{2}}$ appropriate to HA, is observed while at high pH a single wave with $E_{\frac{1}{2}}$ appropriate to A^- is found. At intermediate pH both waves are observed and, although it might be thought that each step arises from the discharge of the equilibrium concentrations of the two species, the fact that the pH region in which the double steps occur is quite far removed from the pK_a of the acid (around which the concentrations of HA and A^- are similar) disproves this. The cause is rather more subtle.

The disadvantage of the rigorous approach to this type of problem is that the mathematics becomes very involved for all except the simplest reaction. Instead, it is common to consider the somewhat vague concept of the 'reaction layer', which gives a mental picture of the processes involved and allows the rate constants of rather more complicated processes to be estimated. The reaction layer is a hypothetical layer surrounding the electrode within which all the HA molecules produced by reaction (2.14) reach the electrode and are reduced. Its thickness μ depends on the rate constant k_d and the diffusion coefficient of A^-, $\mu = (D/k_d)^{\frac{1}{2}}$. Suppose the applied potential is only sufficient to discharge HA, yet the pH is such that the concentration of HA close to the electrode is very small. This small equilibrium concentration will be discharged and equilibrium (2.14) will be disturbed. The concentration of A^- near the electrode will therefore decrease and the total current will consist of a contribution due to the diffusion of A^- across the reaction layer followed by the production of HA and a small contribution due to the diffusion of HA. As the voltage is increased, the (average) current will increase to a maximum value $\bar{i}_k$ which depends on the pH and the relative values of k_d and k_r. As the voltage is increased further the discharge of A^- starts and the remainder of the current-voltage curve is like that found at high pH. The modified form of the Ilkovič equation for this situation is,

$$\frac{\bar{i}_k}{\bar{i}_d} = \frac{0{\cdot}886(k_r K t_m)^{\frac{1}{2}} c_{H^+}}{1 + 0{\cdot}886(k_r K t_m)^{\frac{1}{2}} c_{H^+}}$$

where $K = k_r/k_d$. The recombination rate constant k_r for pyruvate plus a proton was determined by this method to be $1{\cdot}3 \times 10^{10}$ l/mole sec at 25°.

Polarography and the electrochemical methods generally have been used to study the kinetics of many systems. The results usually agree with those measured by other methods but there are some data, for acid–base reactions in particular, which do not agree. In some cases the rate is too low and this may be explained in terms of a reaction preceding the main reaction. In others, however, the rate constant is larger than that calculated for a diffusion-controlled reaction (Chapter 1) and so the results must be regarded with a certain amount of suspicion. The reason for this discrepancy is not clear.

REFERENCES

1. S. L. Friess, E. S. Lewis and A. Weissberger (Eds.), *Technique of Organic Chemistry*, Vol. 8, Part 2, Interscience, New York, 1963.
2. J. T. Haysom and R. H. Prince, to be published.
3. B. Chance, R. H. Eisenhardt, Q. H. Gibson and K. K. Lonberg-Holm (Eds.), *Rapid Mixing and Sampling Techniques in Biochemistry*, Academic Press, New York, 1964.
4. J. Halpern and J. P. Maher, *J. Am. Chem. Soc.*, **87**, 5361 (1965).
5. S. W. Benson and W. B. De More, *Ann. Rev. Phys. Chem.*, **16**, 397 (1965).
6. M. A. A. Clyne and B. A. Thrush, *Proc. Roy. Soc.* (*London*), *A*, **261**, 259 (1961).
7. R. G. W. Norrish and G. Porter, *Nature*, **164**, 658 (1949); R. G. W. Norrish and B. A. Thrush, *Quart. Rev.* (*London*), **10**, 149 (1956); and Ref. 1, p. 1055.
8. G. Porter and M. W. Windsor, *Discussions Faraday Soc.*, **17**, 178 (1954).
9. G. Porter and M. R. Topp, *Nature*, **220**, 1228 (1968); see also J. R. Novak and M. W. Windsor, *Proc. Roy. Soc.* (*London*), *A*, **308**, 95 (1968).
10. K. H. L. Erhard and R. G. W. Norrish, *Proc. Roy. Soc.* (*London*), *A*, **234**, 178 (1956).

11. H. T. Witt, and others, *Angew. Chem. Intl. Edn.*, **4**, 799 (1965); H. T. Witt, *Fifth Nobel Symposium, Fast Reactions and Primary Processes in Chemical Kinetics*, Interscience, New York, 1967, p. 261.
12. L. M. Dorfman and M. S. Matheson, *Progress in Reaction Kinetics* (Ed. G. Porter), Vol. 3, Pergamon, Oxford, 1965, p. 237.
13. S. H. Bauer, *Science*, **141**, 867 (1963); J. N. Bradley, *Shock Waves in Chemistry and Physics*, Methuen, London, 1962; J. N. Bradley, 'Chemical applications' of the shock tube, *Roy. Inst. Chem. (London), Lecture Ser. No. 6*, 1 (1963); S. H. Bauer, *Ann. Rev. Phys. Chem.*, **16**, 245 (1965).
14. R. W. Getzinger and G. L. Schott, *J. Chem. Phys.*, **43**, 3237 (1965); S. H. Bauer, G. L. Schott and R. E. Duff, *J. Chem. Phys.*, **28**, 1089 (1958).
15. A. Jost, *Ber. Bunsenges*, **70**, 1057 (1966).
16. M. Eigen and L. De Maeyer, in Ref. 1, p. 895.
17. G. W. Castellan, *Ber. Bunsenges. Physik. Chem.*, **67**, 898 (1963); R. A. Alberty, G. Yagil, W. F. Diven and M. Takahashi, *Acta Chem. Scand.*, **17**, S34 (1963); K. Kustin, D. Shear and D. Kleitman, *J. Theor. Biol.*, **9**, 186 (1965); G. Czerlinski, *Chemical Relaxation*, Marcel Dekker, New York, 1966; also Ref. 16.
18. G. Czerlinski and M. Eigen, *Z. Elektrochem.*, **63**, 652 (1959); Ref. 16.
19. B. Havsteen, in *Instrumentation in Biochemistry* (Ed. T. W. Goodwin), Academic Press, New York, 1966, p. 53; J. E. Erman and G. G. Hammes, *Rev. Sci. Instr.*, **37**, 746 (1966).
20. H. Strehlow and M. Becker, *Z. Elektrochem.*, **63**, 457 (1959); Ref. 16; H. Hoffman, J. Stuehr and E. Yeager, in *Chemical Physics of Ionic Solutions* (Eds. B. E. Conway and R. E. Barradas), Wiley, New York, 1966, p. 255.
21. G. Ilgenfritz, Thesis, Göttingen, 1966; G. Ilgenfritz and L. De Maeyer, to be published.
22. (a) G. Kurtze and K. Tamm, *Acustica*, **3**, 33 (1953); (b) M. Eigen and K. Tamm, *Z. Elektrochem.*, **66**, 107 (1962).
23. J. A. Pople, W. G. Schneider and H. J. Bernstein, *High-resolution Nuclear Magnetic Resonance*, McGraw-Hill, New York, 1959; A. Carrington and A. D. McLachlan, *Introduction to Magnetic Resonance*, Harper International, New York, 1967.
24. C. S. Johnson, in *Advances in Magnetic Resonance* (Ed. J. S. Waugh), Vol. I, Academic Press, New York, 1965, p. 33.
25. F. Bloch, *Phys. Rev.*, **70**, 460 (1946).
26. E. Grunwald, C. F. Jumper and S. Meiboom, *J. Am. Chem. Soc.*, **84**, 4664 (1962).
27. H. S. Gutowsky and C. H. Holm, *J. Chem. Phys.*, **25**, 1228 (1957).
28. A. Allerhand, H. S. Gutowsky, J. Jonas and R. A. Meinzer, *J. Am. Chem. Soc.*, **88**, 3185 (1966).
29. F. A. L. Anet and A. J. R. Bourn, *J. Am. Chem. Soc.*, **89**, 760 (1967).
30. J. E. Anderson, *Quart. Rev. (London)*, **19**, 426 (1965).
31. Z. Luz, D. Gill and S. Meiboom, *J. Chem. Phys.*, **30**, 1540 (1959).
32. J. T. Arnold and M. E. Packard, *J. Chem. Phys.*, **19**, 1608 (1951).
33. T. J. Swift and R. E. Connick, *J. Chem. Phys.*, **37**, 307 (1962).
34. M. Cohn, *Biochem.*, **2**, 623 (1963).
35. H. Y. Carr and E. M. Purcell, *Phys. Rev.*, **94**, 630 (1954).
36. S. Forsén and R. A. Hoffman, *J. Chem. Phys.*, **39**, 2892 (1963); **40**, 1189 (1964).

37. R. L. Ward and S. I. Weissman, *J. Am. Chem. Soc.*, **79**, 2086 (1957).
38. F. C. Adam and S. I. Weissman, *J. Am. Chem. Soc.*, **80**, 1518 (1958).
39. M. M. Kreevoy and C. A. Mead, *J. Am. Chem. Soc.*, **84**, 4596 (1962); and *Discussions Faraday Soc.*, **39**, 166 (1965); A. K. Covington, M. J. Tait and Wynne-Jones, *Discussions Faraday Soc.*, **39**, 172 (1965).
40. F. A. Matsen, 'Chemical applications of spectroscopy' in *Technique of Organic Chemistry* (Ed. A. Weissberger), Vol. IX, Interscience, New York, 1956, p. 694.
41. T. Förster, *Fluoreszenz Organischer Verbindungen*, Vandenhoek and Ruprecht, Göttingen, 1951; A. Weller, in *Progress in Reaction Kinetics* (Ed. G. Porter), Vol. 1, Pergamon, Oxford, 1961, p. 189.
42. W. Urban and A. Weller, *Ber. Bunsenges. Physik. Chem.*, **67**, 787 (1963).
43. M. Becker and H. Strehlow, *Z. Elektrochem.*, **64**, 129, 813 (1960).

PROBLEMS

1. Reaction (1),

$$A + B \underset{k_b}{\overset{k_f}{\rightleftharpoons}} C \tag{1}$$

initially at equilibrium, is subjected to a rapid perturbation (e.g. a small rise in temperature) which causes a slight displacement in the position of equilibrium. Show that, if this displacement is sufficiently small, the return of the system to equilibrium will follow the first-order rate law (2),

$$\frac{-\mathrm{d}|x|}{\mathrm{d}t} = k'|x| \tag{2}$$

and that the rate constant for this relaxation process is given by (3),

$$k' = k_f(\bar{c}_A + \bar{c}_B) + k_b \tag{3}$$

where $|x|$ is the instantaneous displacement of the concentration of A, B or C from its new equilibrium value ($\bar{c}_A$, $\bar{c}_B$ and $\bar{c}_C$, respectively).

2. Zinc(II) forms a 1:1 complex with pyridine-2-azo-*p*-dimethylaniline (D) according to scheme (1):

$$Zn^{2+} + D \underset{k_b}{\overset{k_f}{\rightleftharpoons}} ZnD^{2+} \tag{1}$$

In a series of temperature-jump experiments, the following values of the apparent first-order rate constant k' (see question 1) were obtained at different total concentrations of zinc:

conc. of Zn^{2+}(M):

$7{\cdot}50 \times 10^{-3}$ $6{\cdot}25 \times 10^{-3}$ $5{\cdot}00 \times 10^{-3}$ $3{\cdot}75 \times 10^{-3}$ $2{\cdot}50 \times 10^{-3}$

k' (sec^{-1}):

$7{\cdot}64 \times 10^4$ $6{\cdot}84 \times 10^4$ $6{\cdot}10 \times 10^4$ $5{\cdot}27 \times 10^4$ $4{\cdot}52 \times 10^4$

In all cases the total concentration of D was 3×10^{-5} M. Evaluate k_f and the stability constant of the complex ZnD^{2+}.

3. Give the expressions for the reciprocal relaxation times corresponding to the following single-step reactions and explain how you would determine the individual rate constants for forward and backward steps in each case.

   (a) $A \rightleftharpoons B + C$,
   (b) $A \rightleftharpoons B + C$ (where the concentration of B is much greater than those of A and C),
   (c) $A \rightleftharpoons B$,
   (d) $2A \rightleftharpoons B$,
   (e) the ionization of an acid in a solution which is buffered at a pH in the neighbourhood of the pK_a of the acid.

4. The formation of many metal complexes does not involve a colour change and can therefore be followed spectrophotometrically only with the help of an indicator.

   In a system involving a metal ion M^{2+}, an anionic ligand L^- and a pH indicator In^-, the following reactions must be considered.

$$M^{2+} + L^- \rightleftharpoons ML^+ \qquad (1)$$

$$\left.\begin{array}{l} HL \rightleftharpoons L^- + H^+ \\ HIn \rightleftharpoons In^- + H^+ \end{array}\right\} \qquad (2)$$

   On the assumption that the protolytic reactions (2) reach equilibrium much more rapidly than the metal complex reaction, derive an expression for the relaxation time associated with reaction (1).

   [G. G. Hammes and J. I. Steinfeld, *J. Amer. Chem. Soc.*, **84**, 4639 (1962)].

5. One method of extending the range of metal complex formation reactions which can be studied by chemical relaxation techniques is to use conditions under which the proton becomes an effective competitor with the metal ion for the anionic ligand—i.e. to use a comparatively low pH. At low pH the bidentate ligand 8-hydroxyquinoline (HOx) reacts with Mn^{2+} by two parallel routes

$$\begin{array}{ccc} HOx + Mn^{2+} & \underset{k_{23}}{\overset{k_{32}}{\rightleftharpoons}} & MnOxH^{2+} \\ k_{43}\Big\uparrow\Big\downarrow k_{34} & & k_{12}\Big\uparrow\Big\downarrow k_{21} \\ H^+ + Ox^- + Mn^{2+} & \underset{k_{14}}{\overset{k_{41}}{\rightleftharpoons}} & MnOx^+ + H^+ \end{array}$$

   On the assumptions (a) that reactions involving protons are rapid, (b) that the concentration of Mn^{2+} is much larger than those of the other species, (c) that the steady-state approximation may be applied to the formation of $MnOxH^{2+}$ but not Ox^-, and (d) that the solution is pH-buffered, derive an expression for the relaxation time for the metal complex formation. (Hint: the algebra is simplified considerably if the two routes from (Mn^{2+} + HOx) to ($MnOx^+ + H^+$) are treated separately and the individual expressions for τ^{-1} summed at the end. This procedure is always permissible for reactions involving parallel pathways.)

   [D. N. Hague and M. S. Zetter, *Trans. Faraday Soc.*, **66**, 1176 (1970)].

6. Derive expressions for the two relaxation effects which are observed in solutions containing of the order of 10^{-4} M Biebrich Scarlet and α-chymotrypsin (Figure 2.11, p. 38). How would you check the interpretation advanced on p. 38 for these effects?

   [D. N. Hague, J. S. Henshaw, V. A. John, M. J. Pooley and P. B. Chock, *Nature*, **229**, 190 (1971).

7. A method for following the binding of a non-coloured inhibitor A at the active site of an enzyme E is to use an indicator I which (a) is also known to bind at the active site and (b) changes colour when it does so

$$E + A \underset{k_{10}}{\overset{k_{01}}{\rightleftharpoons}} EA \tag{1}$$

$$E + I \underset{k_{20}}{\overset{k_{02}}{\rightleftharpoons}} EI \tag{2}$$

   Derive expressions for the two relaxation times for this system when:

   (i) reaction (2) is much faster than reaction (1), and

   (ii) the reactions are of comparable rate.

   What factors, other than the rate constants, determine the feasibility of using this technique with the temperature-jump method for a particular enzyme-inhibitor-indicator system?

8. The exchange of ^{35}Cl between bulk solution chloride and the complex $CoCl_3py^-$ in nitromethane has been followed by line-width measurements. The variation of τ_M, the lifetime of ^{35}Cl in the inner coordination sphere of the metal, with pyridine (py) concentration for dilute solutions of the complex was as follows:

conc. of py(M)	1·00	2·00	3·00	4·00
τ_M (μsec)	88·5	54·6	40·0	31·2

   Deduce the rate law for chloride exchange and evaluate the apparent rate constant(s).

   (The concentration of free chloride was kept constant during this series of experiments.)

   [Data from R. E. Gentzler, T. R. Stengle and C. H. Langford, *Chem. Comm.*, 1257 (1970)].

9. Although lead tetraethyl can be used as an antiknock in internal combustion engines (p. 23), the corresponding tin compound cannot. Why?

   [Ref. 10].

CHAPTER THREE

REACTIONS OF PROTONS, ELECTRONS AND METAL IONS

In this chapter we shall discuss three types of reaction in solution which have been studied by the techniques described in Chapter 2. They are all elementary reactions in the sense used in Chapter 1 and, although there are still various aspects which remain to be clarified, we are now essentially in the position of being able to predict the kinetic behaviour of an unmeasured system from its thermodynamic, or equilibrium, behaviour. We shall consider proton transfer and metal complex formation—both of which have been studied by several of the methods discussed, notably chemical-relaxation technique and n.m.r.—and electron transfer. Although electron-transfer reactions, such as those between two metal complexes, have been studied for many years, we shall be concerned mainly with the recent work involving the hydrated electron; the technique which has been particularly valuable here is pulse radiolysis.

PROTON TRANSFER

In many respects the proton occupies a unique position in reactions occurring in solution. In general, proton-transfer reactions are very fast and the elucidation of their reactivity patterns, largely by Eigen,[1] may be regarded as one of the first major triumphs in chemical relaxation and some of the other methods described in this book. The majority of the work discussed in this section refers to aqueous solutions, though there is evidence that similar considerations could be applied to work involving other protic solvents.

Before considering the general case of proton transfer, let us look at the reaction which may be regarded as the prototype, namely (3.1).

$$H_3O^+ + OH^- \underset{k_d}{\overset{k_r}{\rightleftharpoons}} 2H_2O \tag{3.1}$$

The chemical relaxation time for neutral water has been determined by several methods to be $3{\cdot}5 \times 10^{-5}$ sec at 25°, and this corresponds to a value of $1{\cdot}4 \times 10^{11}$ l/mole sec for k_r. Since the sum of the diffusion co-efficients for H^+ and OH^- in water ($D_{H^+} + D_{OH^-}$) is known from ionic-mobility measurements to be $1{\cdot}45 \times 10^{-4}$ cm^2/sec, it is possible to estimate[2] the reaction distance a from the Debye theory (Chapter 1) on the assumption that the reaction is diffusion-controlled: it comes to about 8 Å. (In fact, certain possibly doubtful assumptions have to be made: for example, that the bulk dielectric constant value of 79 may be used. It could be argued that a lower value should be used, but in that case *a* would be rather larger than 8 Å.) This is a very interesting result because

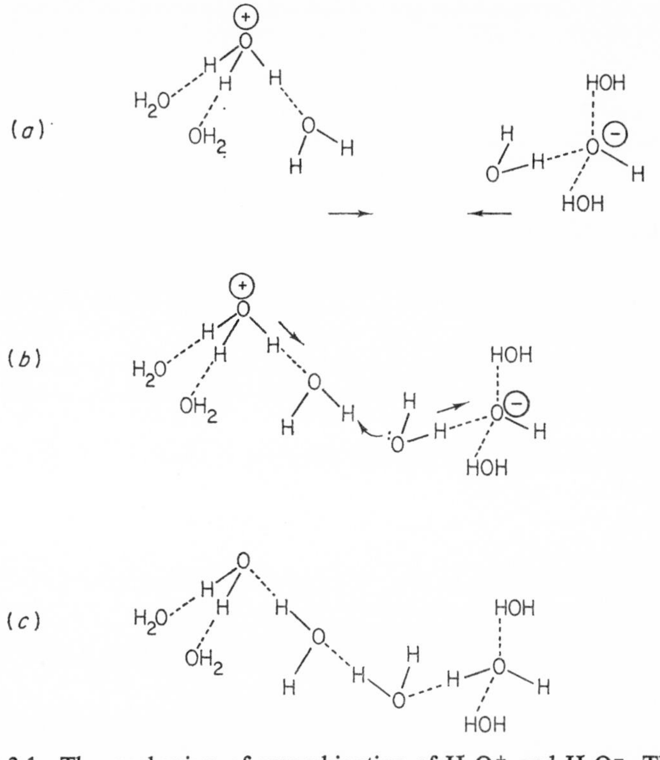

FIGURE 3.1 The mechanism of recombination of $H_9O_4^+$ and $H_7O_4^-$. The ions diffuse together (*a*), a new hydrogen-bond is formed and others are rearranged (*b*), resulting in a neutral 'ice-like' structure (*c*).

a is considerably larger than the sum of the radii of H_3O^+ and OH^-. It actually agrees with the species $H_9O_4^+$ and $H_7O_4^-$, suggesting that these are the reacting species. The proposed mechanism is quite simple (Figure 3.1) and is rather similar to the Grotthus mechanism proposed in 1805 to explain the electrolysis of water. In the first step (a) the hydrated ions, $H_9O_4^+$ and $H_7O_4^-$, diffuse towards each other under the influence of their mutual electrostatic attraction; in the second (b) a hydrogen-bond is formed which bridges the two hydrated ions; in the third (c) a proton is transferred along this hydrogen-bond connexion; and finally (d) the hydrated structure may be destroyed. A fair amount of independent evidence has been obtained for the high stability of such complexes as $H_9O_4^+$ and $H_7O_4^-$, for example from mass spectrometry, so the kinetic result is not unreasonable. On this picture, it would be predicted that the rate of reaction between the excess proton (H_3O^+) and the defect proton (OH^-) in ice would be rather greater than that in liquid water because of the more extensive hydrogen-bonded structure. This is, indeed, the case (Table 3.1).

The essential feature of this mechanism is the delocalization of the proton and defect proton by means of the hydrogen-bonding in the solvent. It explains why k_r for reaction (3.1) is the largest known rate constant for

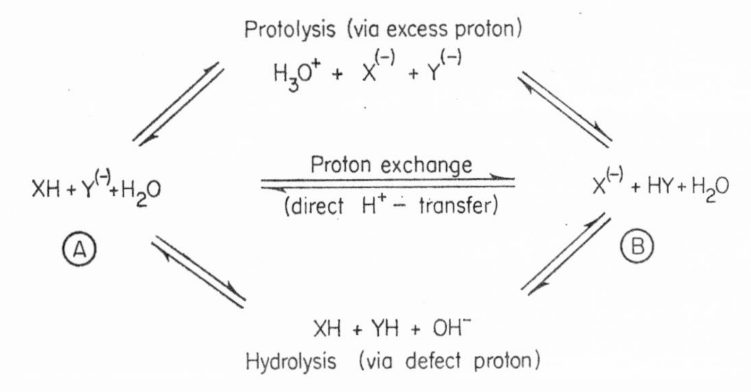

FIGURE 3.2 Reaction scheme for the transfer of a proton between two different acid–base systems in water.

the combination of a unipositive with a uninegative ion in water; it also explains the result, at first sight rather surprising, that reactions of H^+ are generally faster than those of the hydrated electron (see below). The same considerations apply in reactions between H^+ or OH^- and other basis or acids.

Figure 3.2 shows the three possible ways in which a proton can be transferred from XH to $Y^{(-)}$, two of which involve the solvent and one of which does not. In any given situation the important route or routes will be decided by the specific conditions; evidently the important routes are the fastest ones and, since all are second order, all will be concentration-dependent. For example, suppose that HX, $X^{(-)}$, HY and $Y^{(-)}$ are all present in concentrations much greater than 10^{-7} M; this means that at pH around 7 these concentrations are much larger than those of H_3O^+ and OH^- and the direct route is *usually* the most important, both protolysis and hydrolysis being comparatively insignificant. If the pH is

TABLE 3.1 Rate constants for recombination and dissociation reactions involving excess and defect proton in aqueous solution.*

'Normal' reactions in acidic solution	Conditions*	k_r (l/mole sec)	k_d (sec^{-1})
$H^+ + OH^- \rightleftharpoons H_2O$	298, 0	$1{\cdot}4 \times 10^{11}$	$2{\cdot}5 \times 10^5$
$H^+ + OH^- \rightleftharpoons H_2O$ (in ice)	263, 0	$8{\cdot}6 \times 10^{12}$	
$H^+ + F^- \rightleftharpoons HF$	298, 0	$1{\cdot}0 \times 10^{11}$	7×10^7
$H^+ + HS^- \rightleftharpoons H_2S$	298, 0	$7{\cdot}5 \times 10^{10}$	$4{\cdot}3 \times 10^3$
$H^+ + HCO_3^- \rightleftharpoons H_2CO_3$	298, 0	$4{\cdot}7 \times 10^{10}$	$\sim 8 \times 10^6$
$H^+ + SO_4^{2-} \rightleftharpoons HSO_4^-$	293, 0·1	$\sim 1{\cdot}0 \times 10^{11}$	$\sim 1{\cdot}0 \times 10^9$
$H^+ + HCOO^- \rightleftharpoons HCOOH$	298, 0	$\sim 5 \times 10^{10}$	$\sim 8{\cdot}6 \times 10^6$
$H^+ + CH_3COO^- \rightleftharpoons CH_3COOH$	298, 0	$4{\cdot}5 \times 10^{10}$	$7{\cdot}8 \times 10^5$
$H^+ + C_6H_5COO^- \rightleftharpoons C_6H_5COOH$	298, 0	$3{\cdot}5 \times 10^{10}$	$2{\cdot}2 \times 10^6$
$H^+ + o\text{-}H_2NC_6H_4COO^- \rightleftharpoons o\text{-}H_2NC_6H_4COOH$	298, 0	$\sim 5 \times 10^{10}$	6×10^5
$H^+ + m\text{-}H_2NC_6H_4COO^- \rightleftharpoons m\text{-}H_2NC_6H_4COOH$	298, 0	$4{\cdot}8 \times 10^{10}$	$7{\cdot}4 \times 10^5$
$H^+ + p\text{-}H_2NC_6H_4COO^- \rightleftharpoons p\text{-}H_2NC_6H_4COOH$	298, 0	$3{\cdot}5 \times 10^{10}$	$4{\cdot}4 \times 10^5$
$H^+ + (CH_3COCHCOCH_3)^- \rightleftharpoons$ acetylacetone(enol)	298, 0	$\sim 3 \times 10^{10}$	$1{\cdot}7 \times 10^2$
$H^+ + o\text{-}O_2NC_6H_4O^- \rightleftharpoons o\text{-}O_2NC_6H_4OH$	—	$1{\cdot}7 \times 10^{10}$	1×10^3
$H^+ + m\text{-}O_2NC_6H_4O^- \rightleftharpoons m\text{-}O_2NC_6H_4OH$	298, 0	$4{\cdot}2 \times 10^{10}$	$1{\cdot}9 \times 10^2$
$H^+ + p\text{-}O_2NC_6H_4O^- \rightleftharpoons p\text{-}O_2NC_6H_4OH$	298, 0	$3{\cdot}6 \times 10^{10}$	$2{\cdot}6 \times 10^3$
$H^+ + o\text{-}^-OC_6H_4CHO \rightleftharpoons$ salicylaldehyde	298, 0·1	5×10^{10}	3×10^2
$H^+ + NH_3 \rightleftharpoons NH_4^+$	298	$4{\cdot}3 \times 10^{10}$	25
$H^+ + (CH_3)_3N \rightleftharpoons (CH_3)_3NH^+$	298	$2{\cdot}5 \times 10^{10}$	4
$H^+ +$ imidazole $\rightleftharpoons C_3N_2H_5^+$	286, 0·1	$1{\cdot}5 \times 10^{10}$	$1{\cdot}5 \times 10^3$
$H^+ + O{=}C\langle$NH—CO, $^-$N—CO$\rangle C(C_2H_5)_2 \rightleftharpoons$ veronal	298, 0	$1{\cdot}1 \times 10^{10}$	$1{\cdot}2 \times 10^2$

TABLE 3.1 (*continued*)

'Normal' reactions in basic solution	Conditions	k_r (l/mole sec)	k_d (sec^{-1})
$OH^- + NH_4^+ \rightleftharpoons NH_3 + H_2O$	293, 0	$3{\cdot}4 \times 10^{10}$	6×10^5
$OH^- + (CH_3)NH_3^+ \rightleftharpoons (CH_3)NH_2 + H_2O$	293, 0	$3{\cdot}7 \times 10^{10}$	$1{\cdot}6 \times 10^7$
$OH^- + (CH_3)_2NH_2^+ \rightleftharpoons (CH_3)_2NH + H_2O$	293, 0	$3{\cdot}1 \times 10^{10}$	$1{\cdot}9 \times 10^7$
$OH^- + (CH_3)_3NH^+ \rightleftharpoons (CH_3)_3N + H_2O$	293, 0	$2{\cdot}1 \times 10^{10}$	$1{\cdot}4 \times 10^6$
$OH^- + HO(CH_2)_2NH_3^+ \rightleftharpoons HO(CH_2)_2NH_2 + H_2O$	293, 0	$2{\cdot}4 \times 10^{10}$	$9{\cdot}6 \times 10^5$
$OH^- + H_2N(CH_2)_2NH_3^+ \rightleftharpoons H_2N(CH_2)_2NH_2 + H_2O$	293, 0	$3{\cdot}3 \times 10^{10}$	$3{\cdot}3 \times 10^6$
$OH^- + C_3N_2H_5^+ \rightleftharpoons$ imidazole $+ H_2O$	298, 0	$2{\cdot}5 \times 10^{10}$	$2{\cdot}5 \times 10^3$
$OH^- + C_5H_{12}N^+ \rightleftharpoons$ piperidine $+ H_2O$	298, 0	$2{\cdot}2 \times 10^{10}$	3×10^7
$OH^- + {}^+H_3NCH_2COO^- \rightleftharpoons$ glycinate $+ H_2O$	295, 0·5	$1{\cdot}4 \times 10^{10}$	$8{\cdot}4 \times 10^5$
$OH^- + {}^+H(CH_3)_2NCH_2COO^- \rightleftharpoons$ dimethylglycinate $+ H_2O$	295, 0·25	$7{\cdot}3 \times 10^9$	$6{\cdot}5 \times 10^5$
$OH^- +$ phenol $\rightleftharpoons C_6H_5O^- + H_2O$	298, 0	$\sim 1{\cdot}4 \times 10^{10}$	$\sim 1{\cdot}3 \times 10^6$
$OH^- +$ adenine $\rightleftharpoons C_5N_5H_4^- + H_2O$	298, 0	1×10^{10}	$6{\cdot}3 \times 10^5$
$OH^- +$ uracil $\rightleftharpoons C_4N_2H_3O_2^- + H_2O$	298, 0	$9{\cdot}8 \times 10^9$	$2{\cdot}8 \times 10^5$
$OH^- + HCO_3^- \rightleftharpoons CO_2^{2-} + H_2O$	293, 1	$\sim 6 \times 10^9$	—
$OH^- + HPO_4^{2-} \rightleftharpoons PO_4^{3-} + H_2O$	298, 0·1	$\sim 2 \times 10^9$	$\sim 2 \times 10^7$
$OH^- + HATP^{3-} \rightleftharpoons ATP^{4-} + H_2O$	285, 0·1	$1{\cdot}2 \times 10^9$	58

TABLE 3.1 (*continued*)

'Modified' reactions in acidic solution	Conditions	k_r (l/mole sec)	k_d (sec^{-1})
$H^+ + [O{=}C(HN{-}CO)_2CH]^- \rightleftharpoons$ barbituric acid	285, 0·1	1×10^5	10
$H^+ + [(CH_3)_2C(O{-}CO)_2CH]^- \rightleftharpoons$ Meldrum's acid	285, 0·1	$4{\cdot}7 \times 10^5$	7·2
$H^+ + (CH_3COCHCOCH_3)^- \rightleftharpoons$ acetylacetone(keto)	293, 0·1	$1{\cdot}0 \times 10^7$	$2{\cdot}1 \times 10^{-2}$
$H^+ + HSO_3^- \rightleftharpoons SO_2 + H_2O$	293, 0·1	2×10^8	$3{\cdot}4 \times 10^6$
$H^+ + HCO_3^- \rightleftharpoons CO_2 + H_2O$	298, 0·1	$5{\cdot}6 \times 10^4$	$4{\cdot}3 \times 10^{-2}$

'Modified' reactions in basic solution	Conditions	k_r (l/mole sec)	k_d (sec^{-1})
$OH^- + {}^+HN(CH_3)_3 \rightleftharpoons (CH_3)_3N + H_2O$	298, 0	$2{\cdot}1 \times 10^{10}$	$1{\cdot}4 \times 10^6$
$OH^- + {}^+HN(CH_3)_2CH_2COO^- \rightleftharpoons (CH_3)_2NCH_2COO^- + H_2O$	295, 0·25	$7{\cdot}3 \times 10^9$	$6{\cdot}5 \times 10^5$
$OH^- + {}^+HN(CH_3)(CH_2COO^-)_2 \rightleftharpoons (CH_3)N(CH_2COO^-)_2 + H_2O$	298, 0·1	$>10^9$	—
$OH^- + {}^+HN(CH_2COO^-)_3 \rightleftharpoons N(CH_2COO^-)_3 + H_2O$	298, 0·1	$1{\cdot}4 \times 10^7$	$1{\cdot}2 \times 10^3$
$OH^- + HEDTA^{3-} \rightleftharpoons EDTA^{4-} + H_2O$	285, 0·1	$3{\cdot}8 \times 10^7$	$1{\cdot}1 \times 10^4$
$OH^- + p\text{-}NH_2C_6H_3(OH)COO^- \rightleftharpoons p$-aminosalicylate $+ H_2O$	298, 1·0	3×10^7	—

TABLE 3.1 (*continued*)

'Modified' reaction sin basic solution	Conditions	k_r (1/mole sec)	k_d (sec^{-1})
$OH^- + {}^-O$–C_6H_3(OH)–N=N–C_6H_4–NO_2 ⇌ ^-O–$C_6H_3(O^-)$–N=N–C_6H_4–$NO_2 + H_2O$	285, 0·1	$4{\cdot}8 \times 10^5$	5×10^3
OH^- + $C_{10}H_6$(OH)–N=N–C_6H_4–SO_3^- ⇌ orange II + H_2O	285, 0·1	$3{\cdot}6 \times 10^6$	7×10^3
$OH^- + H_3C$–C(=O)–CH=C(OH)–CH_3 ⇌ acetylacetonate + H_2O	285, 0·1	$1{\cdot}9 \times 10^7$	33
OH^- + HC(–C(=O)O^-)=HC(–C(=O)OH) ⇌ maleate + H_2O	285, 0·1	$7{\cdot}4 \times 10^8$	7·4
$OH^- + CH_3COCH_2COCH_3$ ⇌ acetylacetonate + H_2O	293, 0·1	$3{\cdot}8 \times 10^4$	$2{\cdot}7 \times 10^{-1}$
$OH^- + CO_2 \rightleftharpoons HCO_3^-$	298, 0·1	$1{\cdot}4 \times 10^4$	1×10^{-4}

* Data from Ref. 2. Conditions are temperature (°K) and ionic strength.

lowered or raised it is found that the protolysis or hydrolysis path, respectively, becomes more important than previously, and so the reaction will either be a proton exchange coupled with a protolysis or a proton exchange coupled with a hydrolysis (even though the concentration of H_3O^+ or OH^- is still low compared with the others). If the relaxation technique is being used, then the steady-state treatment will be applied for the H_3O^+ or OH^- path when deriving the expression for τ^{-1}. If the pH is lowered or raised further (say, $\lesssim 4$ or $\lesssim 10$, respectively), the concentration of H^+ or OH^- becomes comparable to the others and so the normal two-path treatment is used (section 2.3). We shall consider the protolysis and hydrolysis steps first and then the direct proton transfer.

(a) Protonation and hydrolysis

We can represent these pathways by, respectively, reactions of type (3.2) and (3.3) and make a very simple generalization about them.

$$A^{(-)} + H_3O^+ \underset{k_{b,1}}{\overset{k_{f,1}}{\rightleftharpoons}} AH + H_2O \tag{3.2}$$

$$BH + OH^- \underset{k_{b,2}}{\overset{k_{f,2}}{\rightleftharpoons}} B^{(-)} + H_2O \tag{3.3}$$

If $A^{(-)}$ is a better proton acceptor than H_2O (i.e. it is a weaker acid, a stronger base or has a higher pK—which are all equivalent), then in the forward direction reaction (3.2) is essentially like (3.1) and $k_{f,1}$ is typical of a diffusion-controlled reaction. Similarly, if $B^{(-)}$ is a worse proton acceptor than OH^- (i.e. the pK_a of HB is less than that of H_2O), then in the forward direction reaction (3.3) is like that of H_3O^+ and OH^- and $k_{f,2}$ is typical of a diffusion-controlled reaction. At 25° the ionic product of water is $10^{-14.00}$ M^2 and so, for acids with p$K_a > 7$, reaction (3.2) is diffusion-controlled in the forward direction and, for acids with p$K_a < 7$, reaction (3.3) is diffusion-controlled in the forward direction. In view of the relationship between equilibrium constants and rate constants, the reverse rate constants for these two reactions can readily be determined from the pK_a. Thus, $k_{b,1} = k_{f,1}10^{-\text{p}K_a}$ sec^{-1} and $k_{b,2} = k_{f,2}10^{-(14-\text{p}K_a)}$ sec^{-1}. We might note two other points: since the ionization constant of water is temperature-dependent a slightly different expression is required for $k_{b,2}$ at temperatures other than 25° and, as discussed below, $k_{f,1}$ is rather larger than $k_{f,2}$ (see Table 3.1). We can summarize this picture in the form of Figure 3.4 (p. 93). Similar diagrams may be constructed for protolysis and solvolysis reactions in other protic solvents, e.g. ethanol. The maximum (diffusion-controlled) rate constants would then be modified to take account of the different dielectric constant, hydrogen-bonding properties, and so on.

This simple picture is found for most 'normal' acids; the recombination rate constants lie between 10^{10} and 10^{11} l/mole sec for all of the OH-, NH- and NH^+-type and some of the SH-type acids whose pK_a values lie in the range -1 to $+15$, except for a few cases as discussed below. This generalization is of great value because it makes it possible to predict the kinetic constants of all acid–base systems of this type. Nearly all the groups that occur in natural amino-acids and many other biologically important groups, such as phosphate, sugars, purine and pyrimidine bases (cyclic NH, amino and enolic OH groups), belong to this category.

This is the general picture; what determines whether a particular recombination rate constant $k_{f,1}$ or $k_{f,2}$ is at the upper or the lower end of the range 10^{10} to 10^{11} l/mole sec? We have seen that the encounter frequency between H_3O^+ and $A^{(-)}$ or between OH^- and HB depends on mobility and reaction distance. For both families of reaction, the sum of the mobilities of the reactants is approximately constant. This is because the individual mobilities of the ions H_3O^+ and OH^- are so much larger than those of $A^{(-)}$ and HB that they dominate the diffusion coefficient terms. Similarly, the reaction distances do not vary greatly since they are determined primarily by the large effective sizes of the excess and defect proton. Hence, diffusion-controlled protonations generally have second-order rate constants larger than those of diffusion-controlled deprotonations by a factor of two or three (Table 3.1), reflecting the fact that D_{H^+} is somewhat larger than D_{OH^-}. The charge product of the reacting species also affects the rate and, to a first approximation, a unit decrease in charge product increases the rate by a factor of 2 to 3, irrespective of whether the charge product is positive, zero or negative. At first sight it is surprising that the repulsion between like charges does not have a larger effect on the rate constant. The reason is that the site in a molecule for its recombination with H^+ (or OH^-) is always a lone pair (or a wholly or partly positively charged hydrogen atom) and therefore the charge product is always negative *at the reaction site*. The net positive or negative charge must be concentrated at a more distant part of the molecule and, especially in a solution of moderate ionic strength, the repulsion will be considerably reduced.

Similar variations in rate constant are caused by spatial symmetry and steric factors. For example, F^- is essentially spherosymmetrical whereas in HS^- the symmetry is reduced by a factor of $\frac{3}{4}$ since there are only three lone pairs instead of four. Consequently, the recombination rate constant for H^+ and F^- would be expected to be larger than that for H^+ and HS^-, quite apart from any difference due to the different effective nuclear charges on the two ions (Table 3.1). Also, in carboxylates (e.g. $HCOO^-$, $MeCOO^-$) essentially only one half of the space surrounding the oxygens is 'available' and the rate constants do not exceed about 5×10^{10} l/mole sec. A similar result is found for substituted phenoxides (except for *o*-nitrophenoxide, in which there is a further reduction of two to three, presumably associated with the presence of the bulky NO_2 group close to the O^-).

We have been emphasizing the importance of hydrogen-bonding between the solvated reagent and the excess or defect proton-solvent complex in determining the value of $k_{f,1}$ and $k_{f,2}$, and it follows that any factor which interferes with the hydrogen-bond formation will slow down the reaction. Let us consider two ways in which this might happen.

Effect (i)

This is observed when the proton which is to be lost by combination with OH^- is involved in an *internal* hydrogen-bond and so cannot be hydrogen-bonded to the solvent. A typical example is the salicylate ion (I). Only

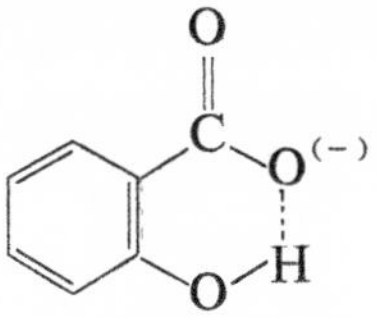

(I)

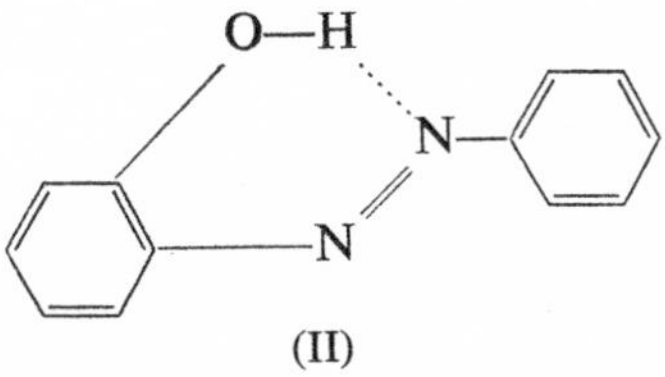

(II)

when the proton has been released from the internal hydrogen-bond can it recombine with OH^-, and a comparison of the k_f for this compound and the similar one in which no internal hydrogen-bonding is possible (e.g. the *para* analogue or the phenol) will give information about the strength of the hydrogen-bond. Further examples are the azo-dyes of the type (II). Table 3.1 indicates that the effect of this on $k_{f,2}$ can be very large. It seems that the strength of the hydrogen-bond and the corresponding reduction in $k_{f,2}$ depend on such factors as the ring size, the planarity and the resonance possibilities.

Effect (***ii***)

This, which may be comparable in size to (***i***), occurs when there is some gross interference with the hydrogen-bonded solvent structure. For example, as the methyl groups of $(CH_3)_3NH^+$ are gradually replaced by CH_2COO^- we would expect a gradual decrease in $k_{f,2}$ because of the increased repulsion between HB and OH^-. This is found to begin with, but when the third CH_2COO^- group has been introduced the geometry of the nitrilotriacetate ion is such that at least one of the three negative carboxylates must come close enough to the H on the nitrogen to perturb the orientation of the water molecules significantly. (It has been shown by i.r. that an internal hydrogen-bond is not responsible for the dramatic decrease in $k_{f,2}$.)

Two other factors can alter the basic kinetic pattern very significantly. It sometimes happens (***iii***) that the molecular structure of the acid and its conjugate base are different, necessitating some gross rearrangement in addition to the transfer of the proton. Also (***iv***), the electron density at the accepting site may be so low that no hydrogen-bond exists between it and the solvent, so that the arrival of the OH^- or H^+ species does not lead automatically to the proton transfer. In both of these cases appreciable activation barriers for the final proton transfer remain and the latter is now the rate-determining step

Effect (***iii***)

As an example of (***iii***) we might consider the hydration of carbon dioxide. Traditionally, this is seen as

$$CO_2 + H_2O \rightleftharpoons H_2CO_3 \rightleftharpoons H^+ + HCO_3^-$$

but such a mechanism is not consistent with the rate data and the mechanism now proposed involves the bicarbonate ion as the intermediate:

$$H_2O + O{=}C{=}O \xleftarrow[\text{slow}]{+H^+} \underset{\text{H—O}\quad\quad \text{O}^-}{\overset{\text{O}}{\overset{\|}{\text{C}}}} \xrightarrow[\text{fast}]{+H^+} \underset{\text{H—O}\quad\quad \text{O—H}}{\overset{\text{O}}{\overset{\|}{\text{C}}}}$$

The decomposition of HCO_3^- to CO_2 is considerably slower than the formation of H_2CO_3 since, although they are both protonations at oxygen-acids, the former is controlled by the rearrangement of the trigonal HCO_3^- into the linear CO_2 molecule whereas the latter is diffusion-controlled.

Effect (*iv*)

This is found in CH- and other 'soft' acids. The CH-acids, often referred to as pseudo acids, have a CH-group next to a polar CX-group. This is often carbonyl and so we can represent the protonation and hydrolysis by Figure 3.3. The deprotonated enol form E^- is a resonance hybrid between the two extremes shown but the form in brackets is not favoured because

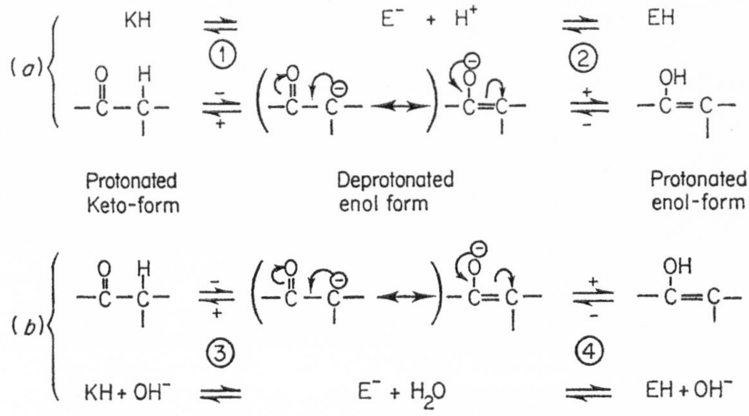

(*a*) $KH \rightleftharpoons E^- + H^+ \rightleftharpoons EH$ (steps (1), (2))

Protonated Keto-form — Deprotonated enol form — Protonated enol-form

(*b*) $KH + OH^- \rightleftharpoons E^- + H_2O \rightleftharpoons EH + OH^-$ (steps (3), (4))

FIGURE 3.3 Protonation (*a*) and hydrolysis (*b*) of a typical CH-acid.

of the lower electronegativity of C compared with O. Thus, steps (1) and (3) are comparatively slow (and in particular the proton transfers in (+1) and (−3) are not now rate-determining) because of the molecular re-arrangement associated with the change of the hybridization at the carbon from sp^3 to sp^2. Note that step (+1) is also retarded by the effect of the lower electron density on the C than on the O (step (+2) is diffusion-controlled), and that step (−3) is also retarded relative to (−4) because CH does not form hydrogen-bonds with the solvent whereas OH does. (Of course, both these effects are caused by the low electronegativity of carbon.)

An example which shows these effects very well is barbituric acid (III) (Table 3.1). As would be expected veronal, the *C*-diethyl substituent of barbituric acid in which there are no acidic CH-groups, has no slow proton-transfer steps: the proton loss in both cases is fast.

In contrast to the 'normal' acids, it is not possible to predict the rate constants for CH-acids although it is sometimes possible to use the very large differences in kinetic behaviour between the two types to determine the relative proportions of the keto- and enol-form in an equilibrium mixture. Such a study has been done with barbituric acid of which, at room temperature, 98·7% is present in the keto-form and 1·3% in the enol-form. Many keto-acids show the type of behaviour we have been

```
        H       O
         \     //
          N—C
         /     \
    O=C         CH2
         \     /
          N—C
         /     \\
        H       O
```

(III)

discussing. Indeed, the rates of ionization are sometimes so low that they can be measured by classical methods. Thus, the ionization of a ketone is frequently the rate-determining step in its halogenation reactions.[3] PH- and SH-acids appear to be closer to CH- than to OH- and NH-acids in their behaviour, although not much work has been done with them yet.

Summary

We can summarize the behaviour found in protolysis and hydrolysis reactions as follows. For 'normal' (hard) acids of the type OH, NH, etc., the prototype reaction between H_3O^+ and OH^- is modified to take account of the somewhat lower diffusion coefficients and different shapes of the acid or base; the recombination rate constant k_r is in the range 10^{10}–10^{11} l/mole sec provided that the reaction is energetically 'downhill', and the reverse rate constant k_d is determined by k_r and the pK_a of the acid. The picture is further modified if some process other than diffusion becomes rate-determining: if, for example, the hydrogen atom is involved in an internal hydrogen-bond; if the hydrogen-bonded structure of the solvent around the site is seriously affected in some way; or if the conjugate acid and base have different geometries. For other (soft) acids of the type CH, etc., both recombination rate constants are considerably less than the diffusion-controlled value because of the significant delocalization of electrons from, for example, the C atom: for the recombination with H_3O^+ the reactivity of the lone pair is too low and for the recombination with OH^- the hydrogen is not hydrogen-bonded to the solvent. In the cases where the deviation from the diffusion-controlled value is very large it is not yet possible to predict the rate constants; in other cases it usually is.

(b) Proton-exchange

Very similar considerations apply here, with the exception that the special 'hydrogen-bond shift' mechanism no longer applies. Again, 'normal' acids and bases undergo diffusion-controlled proton transfer from the weaker to the stronger acceptor—i.e. in reaction (3.4) k_f is diffusion-controlled

$$HX + Y^{(-)} \underset{k_b}{\overset{k_f}{\rightleftharpoons}} HY + X^{(-)} \tag{3.4}$$

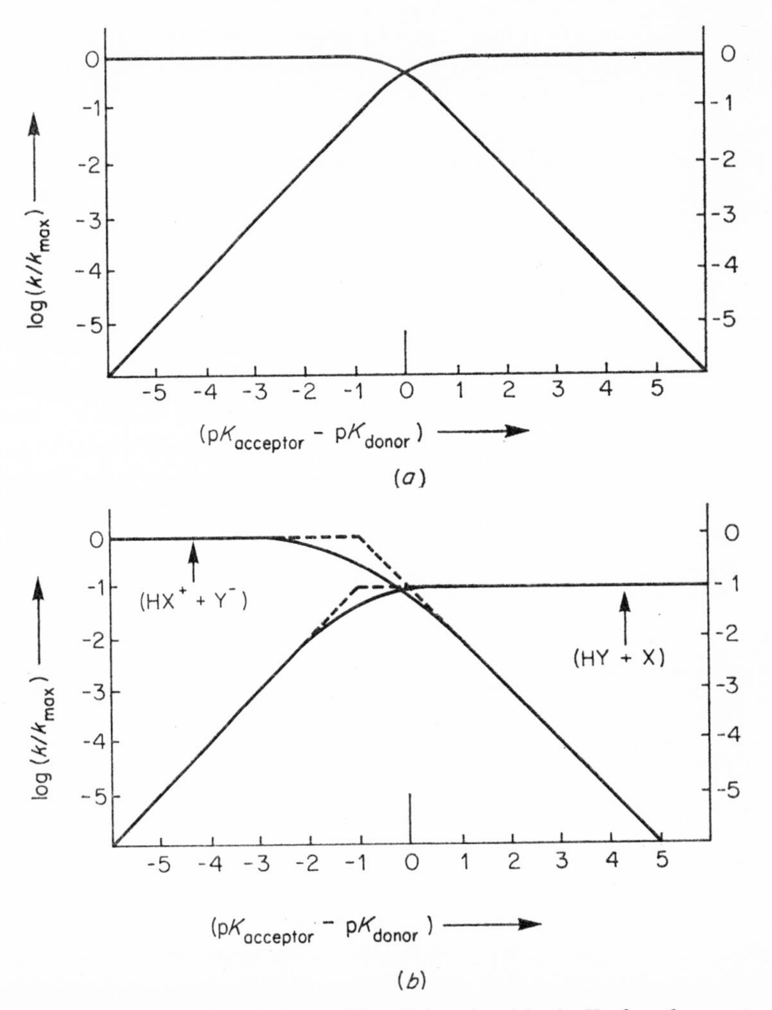

FIGURE 3.4 Idealized variation of $\log (k/k_{max})$ with ΔpK_a for the systems $HX + Y^- \rightleftharpoons HY + X^-$ (*a*) and $HX^+ + Y^- \rightleftharpoons HY + X$ (*b*). k_{max} is the diffusion-controlled value.

if $pK_{HY} > pK_{HX}$ and k_b is diffusion-controlled if $pK_{HY} > pK_{HX}$. The rate will be independent of the difference in pK (ΔpK) but, because the hydrogen-bond shift mechanism involving the solvent does not apply, we would expect the value of the diffusion-controlled rate constant to be rather less than for protolysis and hydrolysis. And in fact it is usually 10^9–10^{10} l/mole sec. Again, the logarithm of the reverse rate constant will be a linear function of ΔpK since $K = k_f/k_b$, and so for a proton exchange between two normal acid–base systems of the same charge type we find the behaviour shown in Figure 3.4(*a*). The two curves cross at $\Delta pK = 0$, when $\log_{10}(k/k_{max})$ is 0·30. [When the two species have the same pK, a symmetrical hydrogen-bond is formed and the proton has a fifty-fifty chance of going one way or the other. Therefore, $\log_{10}(k/k_{max}) = \log_{10} 2$.] If the two acids are not of the same charge type, for example in

$$HX^+ + Y^- \rightleftharpoons HY + X$$

then the limiting values for a diffusion-controlled reaction are different in the two cases (in this case $k_f > k_b$) and so the picture is modified somewhat (e.g. Figure 3.4(*b*)). The diagram may be constructed readily for any normal acid–base system: the maximum rate constant is estimated, the limiting slopes are ± 1 and 0, and the curves cross at $\Delta pK = 0$.

As might be expected, SH-, CH- and other 'abnormal' acids show deviations from this behaviour, but they still follow the same general pattern. For extreme values of ΔpK the slope of the curve tends either to 0 or 1, although the actual value of the limiting rate constant may be very low.

REACTIONS OF THE HYDRATED ELECTRON

It is well known that the deep blue, highly reducing solutions of the alkali metals in liquid ammonia are actually solutions of solvated electrons. Perhaps not so well known is the fact that it is possible, by bombardment with ionizing radiation, to make similar solutions of electrons in water. The hydrated electron reacts very rapidly with many substances but rather slowly with others. Although several hundred reactions of e^-_{aq} have been studied,[4] the great majority by pulse radiolysis, the theoretical aspects are somewhat less well-developed—as is the case, indeed, with the more conventional redox systems, which have been studied for many years, such as those involving electron transfer at transition metal complexes. Before discussing the kinetics, we shall mention some of the work which led to the discovery of e^-_{aq}.

When X-rays, γ-rays and electrons are passed through gases, positive ions and secondary electrons are produced. Weiss suggested in 1944 that when ionizing radiation is passed through liquid water the analogous positive ions and secondary electrons which are produced react further to give hydroxyl and hydrogen free radicals, according to scheme (3.5).

$$\left.\begin{array}{l}\text{Production of oxidizing species:}\\ \qquad H_2O^+ + H_2O \xrightarrow{\text{(i)}} OH + H_3O^+\\ \\ \text{Production of reducing species:}\\ \qquad e^- + H_2O \xrightarrow{\text{(ii)}} H_2O^- \xrightarrow{\text{(iii)}} H + OH^-\end{array}\right\} \quad (3.5)$$

This hypothesis successfully explained the behaviour of irradiated aqueous solutions, but in the early 1950's several workers suggested that step (iii) might not be very fast, and that the hydrated electron H_2O^- (e^-_{aq}) might be playing an important role in the reactions. Indeed, Platzman in 1953 looked at the times and energy changes involved in process (3.5) and concluded that the 'free' electron must spend a significant time in the 'hydrated' state (by 'hydrated', he meant that the electron polarizes the dielectric and is bound in a stable quantum state to it).

What are the times involved? The ionizing radiation loses its high energy in three stages. In the first place a number of electronically excited atoms or molecules, positive ions and fast-moving electrons are produced, so the number of free electrons increases for a short while and as it does so their average energy decreases. At the end of this stage all the particles have energy less than the lowest electronic excitation energy of the medium. The interaction of the primary and secondary radiation with the solution during this first stage is therefore mainly with the electronic systems of the atoms and molecules, and essentially none of the absorbed energy is converted into heat. Since the energy of the electrons is now too low for them to be able to excite the electronic systems of any of the species present, their subsequent interactions must be with atomic motions of various types. In stage two, therefore, the lost energy is converted into heat. In stage three, various thermal reactions take place between the 'stable' products of stage two and other species present in the solution. The latter constitutes the chemical part of the interaction and is the one we shall be concerned with in the bulk of this section. The crux of Platzman's argument, however, concerns the events during stage two.

There are three types of interaction between the 'rather slow' electron of stage two and liquid water: (a) it may interact with the atomic oscillations of the medium, (b) it may interact with the dipolar structure of the medium, and (c) it may undergo elastic scattering. Interactions (a) and (b) are the dominant ones as far as overall energy loss is concerned although

(c) is important in determining the actual path the electron will take in the liquid. The time taken for the secondary electron to become 'thermalized' is of the order of 10^{-13} sec and Platzman estimated that it moves about 1000 Å, finishing up about 50 Å from its (complementary) positive ion. At this stage, the electron is not hydrated in the sense used above, so why can it not undergo reactions (ii) and (iii) of scheme (3.5)? Thermodynamic considerations suggest that steps (ii) and (iii) only become feasible if the significant hydration energy of the hydroxide ion can be used, since the corresponding reactions in the gas phase are distinctly endothermic. However, this hydration energy cannot be used within a time shorter than the dielectric relaxation time of water, which is about 10^{-11} sec. Hence, instead of being captured by and dissociating the water molecule, the electron simply moves on. Platzman therefore predicted that, although the major oxidizing species produced by the interaction of ionizing radiation with liquid water might be the OH radical, the lifetime of the electron must be significantly greater than imagined in view of this Franck–Condon type restriction; it may become so long, in fact, as to make the hydrated electron the major reducing species rather than the H atom produced in reactions (ii) and (iii). This has since been shown to be the case and the overall rate constant of reactions (ii) and (iii) at 25° is actually as low as 16 l/mole sec, which means that the hydrated electron is kinetically surprisingly stable. Thus both e^-_{aq} and H_{aq} are produced and each may subsequently react with oxidants in the solution.

Despite Platzman's predictions, it was almost ten years before the separate existence of the hydrated electron was demonstrated. Several experiments concerning the *G*-values of the different products suggested the existence of a new reducing species of far greater reactivity than the hydrogen atom (the *G*-value is the number of molecules produced per 100 eV absorbed by the solution). The fact that this additional reducing species has a charge of -1 was shown by application of the Brønsted–Bjerrum theory of ionic reactions. If the charge on the reductant is z_r and that on the other reactant is z_s, then the rate constant k will vary with the ionic strength I according to the relationship,

$$\log_{10} k/k_0 = 1{\cdot}02 z_r z_s [I^{\frac{1}{2}}/(1 + \alpha I^{\frac{1}{2}})]$$

where k_0 is the rate constant at zero ionic strength and α is a constant, approximately 1. As shown in Figure 3.5 the results indicate that z_r is -1. Hart and Boag[5] showed by a rapid-scanning spectrographic technique that a strong absorption band in the visible can be identified with the hydrated electron. It is this intense absorption band (Figure 3.6) which allows the reactions of e^-_{aq} to be followed directly, in contrast to those of the other irradiation products of water, such as H, OH, etc.

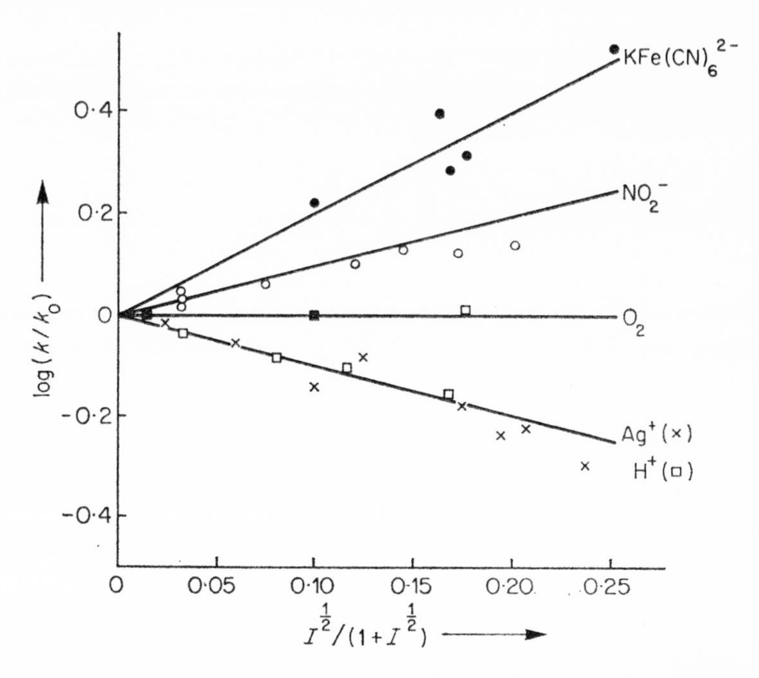

FIGURE 3.5 Effect of ionic strength I on the rate constants for reactions of e_{aq}^- with various solutes (k_0 corresponds to $I = 0$). k, k_0 represent the ratio of rate constants e_{aq}^- with H_2O_2 (N_2O for $KFe(CN)_6^{2-}$ and $CH_2 = CHCONH_2$ for Ag^+) to e_{aq}^- with the solute. The lines are theoretical, assuming $z_r = -1$. [Data from J. H. Baxendale, E. M. Fielden and J. P. Keene, *Proc. Roy. Soc.*, **286A**, 320 (1965); A. Szutka, J. K. Thomas, S. Gordon and E. J. Hart, *J. Phys. Chem.*, **69**, 289 (1965); S. Gordon, E.J. Hart, M. S. Matheson, J. Rabani and J. K. Thomas, *J. Am. Chem. Soc.*, **85**, 1375 (1963).]

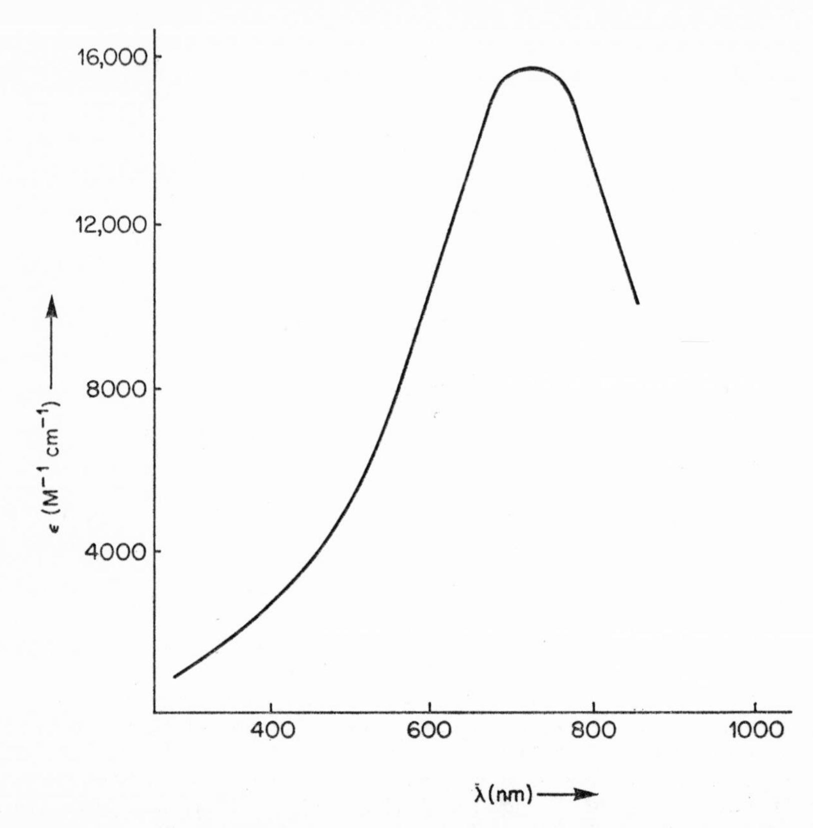

FIGURE 3.6 The absorption spectrum of the hydrated electron. $\lambda_{max} = 720$ nm, $\varepsilon_{max} = 15{,}800 \pm 1600$, and the oscillator strength f is approx. 0·65, which is identical with that of the electron in ammonia. [Data from J. P. Keene, *Radiation Res.*, **22,** 1 (1964) and Ref. 7.]

Decay reactions of e^-_{aq}

It is evident that the decay time of the hydrated electron is a very important quantity since it will not be possible to study reactions which take longer than this.

As we have seen, when water is bombarded with ionizing radiation a complex series of reactions takes place with the released electrons becoming thermalized within about 10^{-13} sec and starting to become associated with particular solvent molecules at about 10^{-11} sec. As this happens the charge becomes spread out over a number of water molecules, and it has been estimated that after about 3×10^{-9} sec the hydrated electron attains its final configuration in solution (cf. IV), with the outer sphere of positive

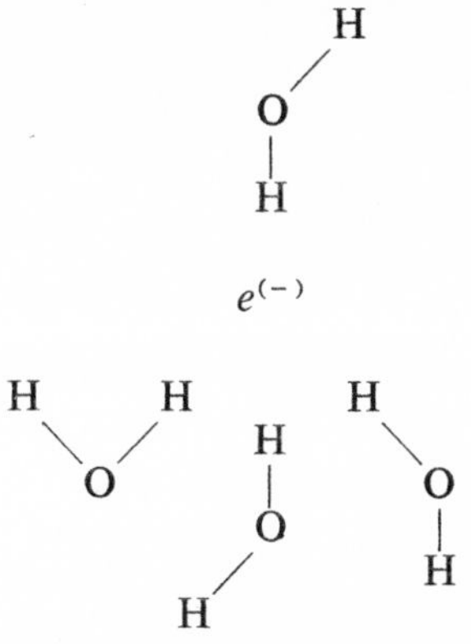

H
O
H

$e^{(-)}$

H H H H
O O O
H H

(IV)

ions which will affect its reactivity towards charged species in the way discussed above (cf. Figure 3.5). After this time, therefore, the products can be represented by the general radiolysis equation, $H_2O \rightsquigarrow (2.6)e^-_{aq}$; (0·5) H; (2·6) OH; (0·45) H_2; (0·7) H_2O_2; (3·6) H_3O^+; (1·0) OH^-, where the numbers are the *G*-values. In other words, in a typical pulse-radiolysis experiment, where a microsecond pulse of γ-rays may be used, we can treat the solution as a homogeneous mixture of these qualities of the various products. Now e^-_{aq} reacts with all of these species except H_2 and OH^-, and the reactions are all approximately diffusion-controlled. The reaction with H_2O itself, whose rate constant is 16 l/mole sec at 25°, gives an absolute lower decay-rate limit with a half-life of approximately 780 μsec. It is usual to work under conditions such that the latter is the limiting reaction but, to ensure this, as many of the other reactive species must be eliminated as quickly as possible.

A commonly used electron-inert additive is methanol, which reacts with H and OH to give the relatively inert CH_2OH radical. Since OH^- is also inert and removes H_3O^+ rapidly, a frequently used solvent is water containing 10^{-3} M methanol and 10^{-3} M NaOH, although it is possible to eliminate the undesirable decay reactions in other ways. For example, in hydrogen-saturated water at pH 8·4 the half-lives of the various important products of irradiation are as shown in Table 3.2. Thus the reaction of OH

TABLE 3.2 Half-lives of reactions occurring in water at pH 8·4 saturated with hydrogen.*

Reaction	Reactant	Concentration (*M*)	$t_{\frac{1}{2}}$
$OH + H_2$	H_2	$0{\cdot}7 \times 10^{-3}$	22 μsec
$H + OH^-$	OH^-	$0{\cdot}25 \times 10^{-5}$	15 msec
$e^-_{aq} + H_3O^+$	H_3O^+	4×10^{-9}	12·5 msec
$e^-_{aq} + H$	H	1×10^{-8}	4 msec
$e^-_{aq} + e^-_{aq}$	e^-_{aq}	7×10^{-9}	14 msec
$e^-_{aq} + H_2O_2$	H_2O_2	5×10^{-9}	17 msec

* Data from Ref. 4(a).

with H_2 is so rapid that this species cannot interfere, while the other reactions are much too slow. If a reactant X is now added at a comparatively large concentration (i.e. $\gtrsim 10^{-9}$ M, which is the approximate concentration of e^-_{aq}) then the kinetics of the reaction (3.6) can be measured

$$X + e^-_{aq} \rightarrow \text{products} \tag{3.6}$$

by following the disappearance of the deep blue colour due to e^-_{aq} *provided* that c_X is such that the half-life of reaction (3.6) is in the range 22–780 μsec.

Other reactions of e^-_{aq}

The rate constants for some reactions of e^-_{aq} are given in Table 3.3 and it will be seen that several are in the range 10^9–10^{10} l/mole sec. Although these values are about an order of magnitude less than the majority of the rate constants for reactions of H_3O^+ and OH^- (Table 3.1), it is appropriate to ask whether they could represent reactions which are diffusion-controlled. For example, is the value of $4{\cdot}5 \times 10^9$ l/mole sec for the

TABLE 3.3 Rate constants for reactions of the hydrated electron.*

Reactant	Matrix and/or OH scavenger	pH	k (l/mole sec)
Non-metallic inorganic compounds			
e^-_{aq}	0·07 M H_2	10·5	$4{\cdot}5 \times 10^9$
H^+	0·5 M ethanol	~4·5	$2{\cdot}3 \times 10^{10}$
H	0·7 M H_2	10·5	$2{\cdot}5 \times 10^{10}$
H_2O	0·7 mM H_2	8·4	16
OH	0·5 M ethanol	10·5	3×10^{10}
H_2O_2	1 mM methanol	~7	$1{\cdot}2 \times 10^{10}$
O^-	0·5 M ethanol	13	$2{\cdot}2 \times 10^{10}$
O_2	1 mM methanol	~7	$1{\cdot}9 \times 10^{10}$
NO	1 mM methanol	~7	$3{\cdot}1 \times 10^{10}$
CO	1 mM methanol	~7	$\sim 1 \times 10^9$
CO_2	1 mM methanol	~7	$7{\cdot}7 \times 10^9$
CS_2	6 mM methanol	7·7	$3{\cdot}1 \times 10^{10}$
HCO_3^-, CO_3^{2-}	—	—	$<10^6$
CN^-	1 mM methanol	11·0	$<10^6$
CNO^-	1 mM methanol	11	$1{\cdot}3 \times 10^6$
CCl_4	1 mM methanol	~7	$3{\cdot}0 \times 10^{10}$
Cl^-	1 mM methanol	10	$<10^5$
ClO^-	—	10	$7{\cdot}2 \times 10^9$
ClO_3^-	—	10	$3{\cdot}5 \times 10^8$
ClO_4^-	—	~10	$<10^6$
I_2	—	~7	$5{\cdot}1 \times 10^{10}$
IO_3^-	1 mM methanol	11	$8{\cdot}3 \times 10^9$
IO_4^-	1 mM methanol	11	$1{\cdot}9 \times 10^{10}$
NO_3^-	—	7·0	$1{\cdot}1 \times 10^{10}$
MnO_4^-	1 mM methanol	13	$3{\cdot}7 \times 10^{10}$
$Cr_2O_7^{2-}$	1 mM methanol	~13	$5{\cdot}4 \times 10^{10}$
Organic compounds			
C_6H_6	1 mM methanol	11	$1{\cdot}4 \times 10^7$
C_6H_5F	1 mM methanol	11	$6{\cdot}1 \times 10^7$
C_6H_5Cl	1 mM methanol	11	$5{\cdot}0 \times 10^8$
C_6H_5Br	1 mM methanol	11	$4{\cdot}3 \times 10^9$
C_6H_5I	1 mM methanol	11	$1{\cdot}2 \times 10^{10}$
C_6H_5OH	1 mM methanol	11	$<4{\cdot}0 \times 10^6$
$C_6H_5CH_3$	1 mM methanol	11	$1{\cdot}2 \times 10^7$

TABLE 3.3 (*continued*)

Reactant	Matrix and/or OH scavenger	pH	k (l/mole sec)
$C_6H_5NH_2$	1 mM methanol	12	$<2 \times 10^7$
$C_6H_5SO_3^-$	1 mM methanol	11	4×10^9
$C_6H_5NO_2$	1 mM methanol	~7	$3{\cdot}0 \times 10^{10}$
C_2H_5OH	—	—	$<10^5$
C_2H_4	—	—	$7{\cdot}6 \times 10^6$
$CH_2{=}CHCH{=}CH_2$	1 mM methanol	~7	8×10^9
adenine	1 mM methanol	7·7	$6{\cdot}2 \times 10^9$
adenosine	—	5	$3{\cdot}1 \times 10^{10}$
cytosine	1 mM methanol	6·0	$\sim 7 \times 10^9$
cytidine	1 mM methanol	12·0	$1{\cdot}2 \times 10^{10}$
thymine	—	6·0	$1{\cdot}7 \times 10^{10}$
uracil	—	6·4	$7{\cdot}7 \times 10^9$
DNA 0·01 % (M.W. 5×10^6)	—	—	10^{12}
Metal ions			
Cr^{2+}	1 mM methanol	6·9	$4{\cdot}2 \times 10^{10}$
Mn^{2+}	—	—	$4{\cdot}0 \times 10^7$
Fe^{2+}	—	—	$3{\cdot}5 \times 10^8$
Co^{2+}	—	—	$1{\cdot}2 \times 10^{10}$
Ni^{2+}	—	—	$2{\cdot}2 \times 10^{10}$
Cu^{2+}	1 mM methanol	~7	$3{\cdot}3 \times 10^{10}$
Zn^{2+}	1 mM methanol	7·1	$1{\cdot}0 \times 10^9$
Cr^{3+}	1 mM methanol	7·1	$6{\cdot}0 \times 10^{10}$
Cd^{2+}	—	~7	$5{\cdot}2 \times 10^{10}$
Pb^{2+}	1 mM methanol	~7	$3{\cdot}9 \times 10^{10}$
Tl^+	—	~7	7×10^{10}
$Co(NH_3)_6^{3+}$	0·2 M NH_3 + 1 mM methanol	11·1	$9{\cdot}0 \times 10^{10}$
$Co(en)_3^{3+}$	1 mM methanol	6·6	$7{\cdot}3 \times 10^{10}$
$Co(en)_2Cl_2^+$	1 mM methanol	5·6	$7{\cdot}1 \times 10^{10}$
$Co(EDTA)^-$	—	—	$2{\cdot}9 \times 10^{10}$
$Co(NO_2)_6^{3-}$	—	—	$5{\cdot}8 \times 10^{10}$
$[Co(CN)_5Cl]^{3-}$	—	—	$1{\cdot}8 \times 10^{10}$
$[Co(CN)_5(NO_2)]^{3-}$	—	—	$8{\cdot}0 \times 10^9$
$Co(CN)_6^{3-}$	—	—	$2{\cdot}7 \times 10^9$

* Data from Ref. 4(a). In all cases the temperature is room temperature (20–25°C).

self-annihilation reaction ($e_{aq}^- + e_{aq}^-$) reasonable? If we assume a value for the diffusion coefficient D of $4{\cdot}5 \times 10^{-5}$ cm^2/sec (which is slightly less than that of the OH^- ion) and apply the Debye formula (Chapter 1), we can calculate a value for the distance of closest approach of the two electrons. This corresponds to an encounter radius for e_{aq}^- of about 3 Å, which is perfectly reasonable. From the temperature coefficient of the rate constant over the range 10–50° an apparent activation energy of approximately 5·2 kcal/mole has been estimated. The similarity with the activation energy for the self-diffusion coefficient of water over a similar range (6·4 kcal/mole at 0° and 3 kcal/mole at 50°) also suggests that this reaction *is* diffusion-controlled. How do the other reactions compare?

Several small species, charged and neutral, react with rates which are more or less comparable, including H, OH, NO, CS_2, CCl_4, NO_3^-, O^-, MnO_4^- and $Cr_2O_7^{2-}$. If we compute the effective radius of e_{aq}^- for these reactions, assuming a reasonable contribution from the other species to the encounter distance, we find it to be rather variable, although always of the order of a few Ångstrom. This implies that these reactions are essentially diffusion-controlled, but that there are still some uncertainties about the finer points of the mechanism.

On the other hand, it is interesting to compare the reactivity of the hydrated proton H_3O^+ towards e_{aq}^- and towards OH^- since the latter is noticeably higher ($2{\cdot}3 \times 10^{10}$ and $1{\cdot}4 \times 10^{11}$ l/mole sec, respectively). If we were to assume that the former reaction is also diffusion-controlled then, assuming that the effective radius of $H_9O_4^+$ is 4 Å and taking into account the high diffusion coefficient of H^+ in water, we would expect a limiting recombination rate constant of $1{\cdot}1 \times 10^{11}$ l/mole sec for $H_3O^+ + e_{aq}^-$. This reaction is therefore, rather surprisingly, *not* diffusion-controlled. It has been suggested that it is not a simple proton transfer from the hydrated H^+ ion to the electron but rather involves the transfer of the electron from its cavity to the $H_9O_4^+$ ion to produce a hydrated hydrogen atom,

$$H_9O_4^+ + (H_2O)_n^- \rightarrow nH_2O + H_9O_4$$

If the transfer of the electron were the rate-limiting step, it might be that this is comparatively slow because the positive charge of the excess proton $H_9O_4^+$ is delocalized over a large number of atoms. Most reactions of e_{aq}^- have rate constants considerably below the diffusion-controlled value.

Thus several reactions of e_{aq}^- are probably diffusion-controlled, but the majority are not. Is it possible to make any further generalizations about these reactions and, in particular, to predict which ones are likely to approach the diffusion-controlled limit?

Some reactions can be excluded on thermodynamic grounds, as in the case of proton transfers (p. 87). If the free energy change for the reaction (3.7) is positive,

$$X + e^-_{aq} \rightarrow X^{(-)}_{aq} \tag{3.7}$$

(i.e. the reaction is thermodynamically unfavourable) then it cannot be diffusion-controlled. The redox potential of the hydrated electron is $-2{\cdot}7$ V, so we can say that if $X^{(-)}$ is a better reducing agent than e^-_{aq} (i.e. the redox potential for the $X/X^{(-)}$ couple is more negative than $-2{\cdot}7$ V) then e^-_{aq} will not reduce X. This is so for the alkali and heavier alkaline earth metals and therefore, in solutions of their salts, these metals are not reduced by the hydrated electron. If, on the other hand, the free energy change for reaction (3.7) is large and negative, then it is potentially diffusion-controlled.

In the case of polyatomic species it is possible and sometimes even likely that the primary products $X^{(-)}_{aq}$ will decompose or react further, for example, with water. The energetics of this reaction would then have an influence on reaction (3.7) (see p. 95). Unfortunately, it is rather difficult to obtain information about these subsequent reactions because of the way in which the reactions of e^-_{aq} are followed. In pulse radiolysis it is usually only possible to see the decay of e^-_{aq}, and so there is no spectral change associated with the secondary reactions; in the earlier work using competition methods, it was only possible to estimate the final products, and so a complex mechanism was very difficult to split up into its component steps. If the kinetics of the appearance of the final product or an intermediate can be studied directly then these difficulties are largely overcome.

(i) *Reactions with organic compounds*

Saturated hydrocarbons, alcohols, amines and ethers are unreactive towards e^-_{aq}. This is hardly surprising since there are no vacant low-lying orbitals in these compounds to accommodate the additional electron. This lack of reactivity of the alcohols and amines is emphasized by the fact that they can be used as solvents for the solvated electron and indeed the lifetime of e^- is rather longer in alcohols and amines than in water.

Olefins are moderately reactive towards e^-_{aq}, and this reactivity is enhanced by conjugation. A good indication of the reactivity of e^-_{aq} towards unsaturated compounds may be had by treating it as a very efficient nucleophile. Benzene itself is relatively unreactive, but the reactivity can be greatly increased by suitable substitution. It has been found that the Hammett σ-function, which is a good measure of the electron-donating and -withdrawing power of a group, correlates well with the rate constant k of reaction (3.7). Thus $\log k$ increases linearly with σ for substituted benzenes over four orders of magnitude of k, as shown in Figure 3.7. The probability of formation of a positive centre in the ring is inversely proportional to the density of the π-electrons, just as the probability of electrophilic attack is directly proportional to it. It will be noted that Br and I facilitate absorption of the electron into the ring to a greater extent than

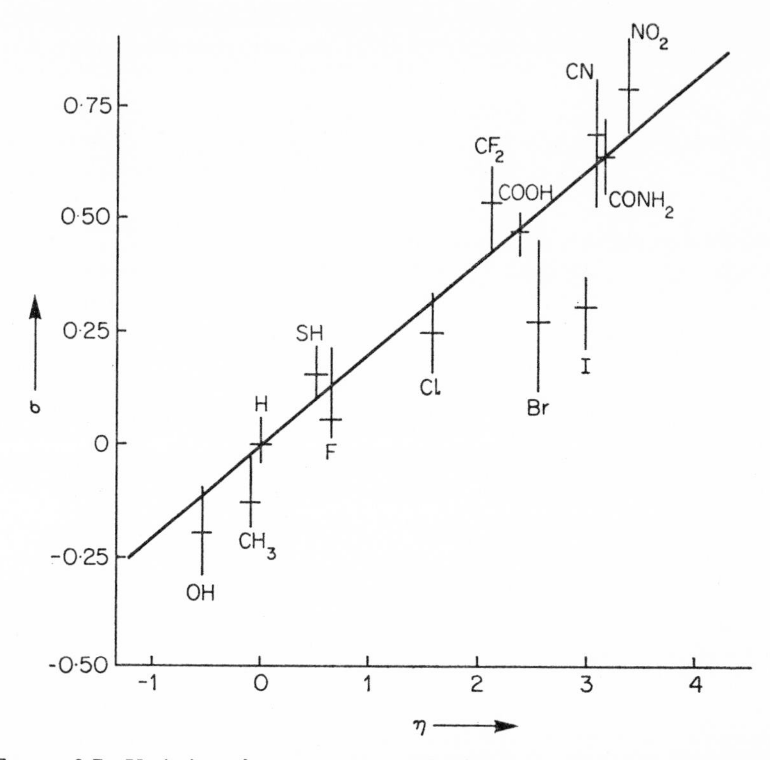

FIGURE 3.7 Variation of rate constant with Hammett σ-factor for reactions of e_{aq}^- with substituted benzenes. $\eta = \log(k/k_B)$, where k_B is the rate constant for the reaction with benzene. [Data from M. Anbar and E. J. Hart, *J. Am. Chem. Soc.*, **86**, 5633 (1964).]

would be predicted on the basis of their contribution to the π-electron density in the ring. It has been suggested that they are acting as bridges for the electron transfer, as they appear to do in electron-transfer reactions between transition metal complexes.[6]

It is particularly interesting to find that purines and pyrimidines are very reactive towards the hydrated electrons, the rate constants being around 10^{10} l/mole sec and therefore in the diffusion-controlled range. This is of great relevance in the biological situation since their reactivity is still high when they are converted into nucleosides, nucleotides, or even DNA. The high rate constants are consistent with the observation that nucleic acids are very sensitive towards ionizing radiation.

(ii) *Reactions with metal complexes*

With the exception of the alkali and heavier alkaline earth metals, which cannot react because of unfavourable free energies, metal ions and complexes can be reduced by e^-_{aq}. The rate constants vary from 7×10^{10} for Tl^+ to $4{\cdot}0 \times 10^7$ l/mole sec for Mn^{2+}, but it is not possible to correlate the reactivity of a metal ion with its redox potential. Not surprisingly, there is also no apparent correlation between rate and the electron affinity of the free metal ion. It has been suggested[7] that the parameters which are important in determining the reactivity of a complex with e^-_{aq} are the availability of a vacant *d*-orbital on the metal and the energy gain on adding the electron.

If we consider the aquo ions in the latter part of the first transition series [Cr^{2+} to Zn^{2+}, Table 3.3(iii)], we see that the reactivity towards e^-_{aq} is highest for Cr^{2+} and Cu^{2+}. This can be rationalized in terms of the fact that the product has either a half-filled (Cr^+, d^5) or a completely filled (Cu^+, d^{10}) 3*d* subshell and therefore enjoys a certain degree of electronic stabilization. In contrast, the reactivities of the high-spin d^5 and d^{10} ions, Mn^{2+} and Zn^{2+}, are comparatively low because they themselves are likewise stabilized.

The replacement of water by other ligands may affect the reactivity of the metal ion in two ways. In the first place, the ligand field splitting of the *d*-orbitals is altered. Thus metals with high-field ligands such as CN^- will tend to change the spin distribution in the *d*-orbitals, favouring the low-spin state. We should expect that $Fe(CN)_6^{4-}$ would be quite unreactive towards e^-_{aq} ($k < 10^7$ l/mole sec) because the additional electron has to enter a vacant e_g orbital with considerably higher energy than the t_{2g} orbitals containing the remaining *d*-electrons. This may explain the general tendency of cyano-complexes to be less reactive than aquo- or halo-complexes. On the other hand, $Mn(CN)_6^{4-}$ should be more reactive than hydrated Mn^{2+} in view of the spin coupling which makes the accommodation of the extra electron easier ($k = 2{\cdot}5 \times 10^{10}$ l/mole sec). The second effect of replacing water by other ligands is to alter the reactivity by acting as a bridge in the electron transfer process. This is especially important for ligands which do not interact strongly with the *d*-orbitals, such as the halides (see above). The efficiency of ligands in this group appears to fall off in the order

$$I > Cl > F > H_2O > NH_3 \sim RNH_2 > CN > OH$$

If we compare the reactivities of two metals in the same group we find that the one with the higher atomic weight is more reactive. Thus Cd^{2+} is more reactive than Zn^{2+}, Pd^{2+} than Ni^{2+} and Pb^{2+} than Sn^{2+}. This is probably connected with the greater availability of the vacant orbitals as well as the increased polarizability of the molecule containing the metal.

It seems, therefore, that the reaction of e^-_{aq} with a metal complex does not involve the metal–ligand bonds directly. The electron appears to undergo rapid tunnelling from its cavity in the solvent to reach its new position (usually in a *d*-orbital) on the metal ion before any other rearrangements take place. These reactions can be seen as elementary steps in the electron-transfer reactions between two transition metal complexes. In view of the many admirable discussions of the inner and outer-sphere mechanisms of these reactions[6,8] we shall not consider them further here. Suffice it to report that the reactivity of different metal complexes towards e^-_{aq} appears to be in good agreement with the modern theories of these more classical electron-transfer reactions.[9]

Summary

We can therefore summarize the behaviour of the hydrated electron by saying that it reacts rather as might be expected. The rate is determined by the availability of a vacant orbital on the other reactant and also by the type of orbital; if the energy of the orbital is favourable and the electron can enter it reasonably easily, then the reaction will approach the diffusion-controlled limit. It was originally thought that the majority of these fast reactions were, in fact, diffusion-controlled because their activation energies all appeared to be about 3·5 kcal/mole (the energy of activation for self-diffusion in water). Recent, more accurate determinations suggest[10] that this is not so, and a value of 1·7 kcal/mole has been found for the reaction with H^+_{aq} and 6·7 kcal/mole for the reaction with H_2O. This confirms the suggestion that most reactions are a little too slow to be diffusion-controlled.

The primary product AB^- may be stable and appear as the final product, but more frequently it is not, and dissociates to give a stable negative ion B^- and a radical A or a stable molecule A and a radical ion B^-. With acids, for example, the radical ion HA^- is the primary product and this usually decomposes. If HA is an oxyacid, the products may be either an H atom and the anion of the acid or an OH^- ion and a free radical from the acid:

$$HOA + e^-_{aq} \rightarrow HOA^- \rightarrow \begin{cases} H + OA^- \\ OH^- + A \end{cases}$$

Generally, the hydration energy of OH^- is greater than that of the acid anion and the free energy of formation of the corresponding free radical is lower than that of a hydrogen atom. Consequently, the products are usually A and OH^-. However, if the acid is $H_2PO_4^-$, the other products are preferred, namely H and HPO_4^{2-}. This is because the dissociation energy of a P—O bond in phosphate is considerably higher than that of an OH bond.

METAL COMPLEX FORMATION

In aqueous solution, metals usually exist as positive ions surrounded in some regular fashion by water molecules. The water molecules in the first (innermost) coordination sphere may be replaced by other groups containing lone pairs of electrons (ligands) to form metal complexes. We shall discuss the ways in which the properties of the central metal, such as charge, size and electronic configuration, affect the binding of the ligands and the inner-sphere water molecules and, therefore, the rate of formation of the complex.

Complexes of certain metals, including Cr^{III}, Co^{III} and Pt^{II}, are non-labile and they have been the subjects of many kinetics investigations. The results of these studies, which have usually been made with the help of conventional spectrophotometric techniques, have been discussed in terms of S_N1 and S_N2 displacements at the metal centre. Langford and Gray[11] have used a somewhat different terminology in which they distinguish between the 'stoichiometric' and 'intimate' mechanisms of complex formation. However, until the advent of the rapid techniques—and in particular relaxation methods—it was not possible to discuss complex formation for the majority of metals, other than to report that it was instantaneous. Although there is still discussion as to the exact mechanism of complex formation, it is possible to make some very interesting generalizations at this stage.

Complex formation of a metal ion with a multidentate ligand (i.e. a ligand which binds at several places to a single metal ion) in water is usually discussed in terms of a three-step mechanism of the type shown in Figure 3.8.

(a) The hydrated metal ion M_{aq}^{n+} and the hydrated ligand L_{aq} diffuse together rapidly to form what is known as an 'outer-sphere' complex (or sometimes, less correctly, an 'ion-pair') in which the lone pairs on the ligand are separated from the metal ion by the inner coordination sphere of the metal. The water surrounding the ligand, being generally less strongly held than that surrounding the metal, is displaced more readily. This first step can therefore also be regarded as a composite one made up of two: diffusion and water loss at the ligand.

(b) The loss of the first water molecule from the inner coordination sphere of the metal coupled with the formation of an M—L bond.

(c) The loss of a sufficient number of the remaining water molecules at the metal to allow the ligand to bind to its full extent.

Metals can be classified according to the relative rates of steps (a) and (b). Group A contains metal ions which have a comparatively low charge density at their surface, i.e. the alkali metals (including Li^{+}) and the heavier alkaline earths, namely Ca^{2+}, Sr^{2+} and Ba^{2+}. The water molecules are held comparatively weakly, with the result that steps (a) and (b) have comparable rates. Group B contains metals of intermediate surface charge density in which the water molecules are held moderately strongly, so that step (b) is now rather slower than step (a). This group includes many bivalent metals, such as Mg^{2+}, Fe^{2+}, Co^{2+} and Ni^{2+} Group C contains metal ions of sufficiently high surface charge density that the water molecules are very strongly held and another reaction can occur before water loss, such as hydrolysis (proton loss) in Al^{3+} and Be^{2+}. This group includes the small highly charged ions and we shall consider it no further except to point out that the substitution rate seems to be dependent on the basiicty of the incoming ligand. Substitution at the hydrolysed ion $M(OH)^{(n-1)+}$ is faster than at the non-hydrolysed ion M^{n+} and so anything which promotes hydrolysis will also promote substitution.

There are, as yet, insufficient data to be sure of the exact mechanism of metal complex formation, and it might even not be meaningful to try and distinguish between an S_N1- and an S_N2-type process at a labile metal ion, since complex formation is almost certainly a concerted process in which water and the incoming ligand change places. However, we shall discuss the metals in Groups A and B further in terms of the general pattern we have outlined.

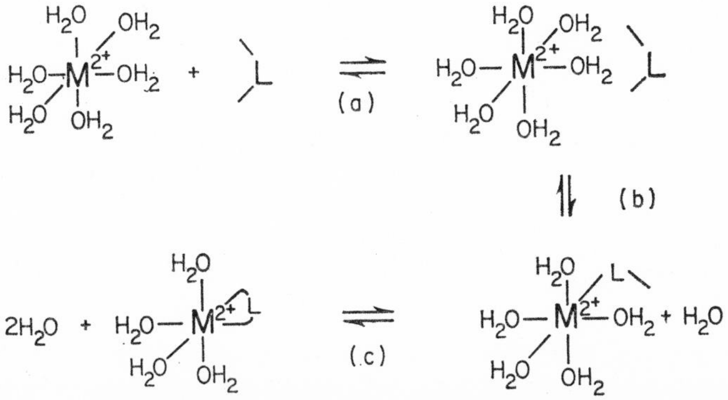

FIGURE 3.8 Mechanism of formation of a complex between a hydrated metal ion [e.g. $M^{2+}(OH_2)_6$] and a bidentate ligand L.

Most Group A metal ions have the d^0 electronic configuration of the rare gases and the interaction of the metal with a ligand is primarily electrostatic in nature. Because the charge density ($\propto$ charge/radius) is small, the water molecules are weakly held and the rate of their loss is high—comparable to the diffusion-controlled value of 10^9–10^{10} sec^{-1}. Comparatively little work has been done on this group. In addition to the difficulties associated with the high rates, there is also the practical problem that the complexes have such low stability constants that they are difficult to detect. This problem has been overcome by using multidentate ligands such as ethylenediaminetetraacetate ($EDTA^{4-}$) and other aminopolycarboxylates, but this means that step (c) (Figure 3.8) is likely to complicate matters.

Table 3.4 shows the results of an ultrasonic relaxation investigation into the formation of complexes of the alkali metals with various ligands. Because steps (a), (b) and (c) all have comparable rates, we find that the overall formation rate constant varies quite considerably with the nature of the ligand. The rate increases gradually as the ionic radius of the metal increases (i.e. as the charge density on the metal ion decreases), and decreases as the number of binding groups on the ligand increases (i.e. it depends on the number of water molecules being substituted). Very similar behaviour is found for Ca^{2+}, Sr^{2+} and Ba^{2+}. Thus the formation rate constant generally corresponds to a water-exchange rate constant of the order of 10^8–10^9 sec^{-1}. Again, it apparently increases somewhat as the radius of the ion increases, and is also dependent on the nature of the ligand.

The behaviour of metals in Group A can be summarized thus: for a metal with a given charge, the discrimination in the formation rate constant is determined primarily by the number of binding groups on the ligand and to a much lesser degree by the nature of the metal. But we can say that to a large extent the stability of the complex is reflected in the *dissociation* rate constant rather than the formation rate constant.

There are many situations, especially in biological systems, in which this result could be of great significance. For example, in the uramil-diacetate (UDA^{3-}) complexes of the lighter alkali metals the stability constants K vary in the order $Li^+ > Na^+ > K^+$, which is opposite in direction to the variation of the formation rate constant k_f; and the discrimination in terms of K is very much greater than that in terms of k_f (Table 3.4(*b*)). This implies that the discrimination in terms of the *dissociation* rate constant must be still higher, and it provides a way of differentiating between the metals in biological systems such as in transport phenomena through membranes. Thus the lifetimes of the Li^+ and Na^+ complexes of UDA^{3-} are longer than the microsecond or so it would take to diffuse through 100 Å, which is the typical thickness of a double

TABLE 3.4

(*a*) Substitution rates of the alkali metal ions

	$EDTA^{4-}$ $[—CH_2N(CH_2COO^-)_2]_2$ τ^{-1} (sec^{-1})	NTA^{3-} $N(CH_2COO^-)_3$ τ^{-1} (sec^{-1})	IDA^{2-} $HN(CH_2COO^-)_2$ τ^{-1} (sec^{-1})	TP^{5-} $P_3O_{10}^{5-}$ k (l/mole sec)
Li^+	$4{\cdot}8 \times 10^7$	$4{\cdot}7 \times 10^7$	$2{\cdot}5 \times 10^8$	9×10^8
Na^+	$4{\cdot}7 \times 10^7$	$8{\cdot}8 \times 10^7$	$2{\cdot}8 \times 10^8$	$>2 \times 10^9$
K^+	$7{\cdot}5 \times 10^7$	$1{\cdot}5 \times 10^8$	—	$>5 \times 10^9$
Rb^+	$1{\cdot}4 \times 10^8$	$2{\cdot}3 \times 10^8$	—	$>5 \times 10^9$
Cs^+	$2{\cdot}1 \times 10^8$	$3{\cdot}5 \times 10^8$	—	$>5 \times 10^9$

Conditions: ionic strength = 0·5 M ($(CH_3)_4NCl$), pH > 11, temperature = 20°C.

(*b*) Rate and equilibrium constants for uramildiacetate complexes of alkali metal ions

	k_{sub} (sec^{-1})	k_{diss} (sec^{-1})	log K_{stab}
Li^+	1×10^8	4×10^2	5·4
Na^+	5×10^8	$2{\cdot}5 \times 10^5$	3·3
K^+	1×10^9	1×10^7	~2·0

Data from M. Eigen and G. Maass, *Z. physik. Chem., N.F.*, 49, 163 (1966). Uramildiacetate is

```
H       O
 \     //
  N—C
 /     \
O=C        C—N(CH2COO-)2
 \     //
  N—C
 /     \
H       O-
```

membrane, whereas the lifetime of the K^+ complex is less than this. Consequently, the potassium complex would dissociate before it had had time to pass through the membrane, whereas those of the lighter metals would not. This is obviously only a very crude model for an ion-transport system, but it does illustrate the way in which kinetic discrimination could work in a biological medium which may contain several chemically similar species. It will be discussed further in Chapter 4.

With Group B metal ions, step (b) is considerably (i.e. >10 times) slower than step (a). We therefore have a fast preequilibrium step followed by the rate-limiting loss of a water molecule from the inner coordination sphere of the metal; and, to a first approximation, the observed overall formation rate constant k_f is given by $k_f = K_{os}k_{23}$, where K_{os} is the equilibrium constant for the formation of the outer-sphere complex and k_{23} is the rate constant for the water-loss process. k_{23} is essentially the rate constant for the water exchange at a metal ion, which can usually be measured independently by n.m.r. when M^{n+} is paramagnetic (see page 58), so this allows a certain check on the mechanism. Unfortunately, K_{os} cannot be measured directly, so it has not yet been possible to confirm the mechanism unequivocally, although the values of k_f do appear to be more or less typical of the metal (Table 3.5) and similar to the water-exchange rate. K_{os} is often similar to the value calculated on the basis of the Fuoss[12] equation

$$K = (4\pi Na^3/3000) \exp(-U(a)/\mathbf{k}T)$$

where $U(a)$ is the Coulomb energy, N the Avogadro number, $\mathbf{k}$ the Boltzmann constant and a the distance of closest approach of the hydrated metal ion and the ligand, taken as 5 Å. (This formula is only applicable to charged ligands but a similar one has been derived for neutral ligands.[13]) On the other hand, the ligand seems to influence k_f to a certain extent (see Table 3.5) and in some cases there is a spread of two or three orders of magnitude, which is not easy to explain in terms of a variation in K_{os}; in the case of certain multidentate ligands some of this variation has been explained in terms of step (c), though in others step (c) appears to be fast compared with step (b). Also, the activation energy of complex formation is sometimes several kcal/mole different from that of the water-exchange process, indicating that the two rates will be very different at temperatures widely different from 25°.

We might mention two other points concerning the formation of complexes of metals in Group B. As for those in Group A, the forward rate constant is approximately inversely proportional to the ionic radius for metals of a given charge type. Secondly, considerable complication can arise because of partially filled d-orbitals on the metal ion. Figure 3.9

TABLE 3.5 Rate constants for the formation of transition metal complexes in aqueous solution.*

Metal ion	Ligand	log k_f	Method
Mn^{2+}	Cl^-	7·2	ESR
	NTA^{3-}	8·7	E
	$HNTA^{2-}$	5·3	E
Fe^{2+}	NO	5·7	TJ
	2,2′-dipyridyl	5·2	SF
	o-phenanthroline	5·9	SF
Co^{2+}	NH_3	5·0	TJ
	2,2′-dipyridyl	4·8	SF
	o-phenanthroline	5·5	SF
	PADA	4·6	TJ
	glycylglycinate⁻	5·7	TJ
	murexide⁻	5·2	TJ
	$malonate^{2-}$	7·0	TJ
Ni^{2+}	NH_3	3·2	TJ
	pyridine	3·7	SF
	imidazole	3·7	TJ
	PADA	3·6	TJ
	glycylglycinate⁻	4·3	TJ
	SCN^-	3·7	SF
	murexide⁻	3·5	TJ
	$oxalate^{2-}$	4·8	SF
	$succinate^{2-}$	5·6	PJ
Cu^{2+}	2,2′-dipyridyl	7·0	SF
	PADA	8·0	TJ
	murexide⁻	8·1	TJ
Zn^{2+}	NH_3	6·5	TJ
	2,2′-dipyridyl	6·0	SF
	o-phenanthroline	6·3	SF
	PADA	6·6	TJ
	murexide⁻	7·3	TJ
Cd^{2+}	*o*-phenanthroline	7·0	SF
	PADA	7	TJ
	Br^-	9·1	NMR
	CN^-	9·6	E
	murexide⁻	8·1	TJ
	NTA^{3-}	10·3	E

* Data are from Refs. 15(b) and 15(d); the majority refer to the second-order rate constant at 25°. The ligands NTA^{3-} and PADA are nitrilotriacetate and pyridine-2-azodimethylaniline, respectively. The methods used include electrochemical (E), stopped-flow (SF), temperature-jump (TJ) and pressure-jump (PJ).

shows the water-exchange rate at various M^{2+} ions of the first long period of the Periodic Table. The increases in rate constant on going from V^{2+} to Cr^{2+} (d^3 to d^4) and from Ni^{2+} to Cu^{2+} (d^8 to d^9) have been rationalized in terms of the Jahn–Teller effect; thus in octahedral Cr^{2+} and Cu^{2+} there are two axial water molecules which are less firmly held than the four equatorial water molecules and the incoming ligand is supposed to

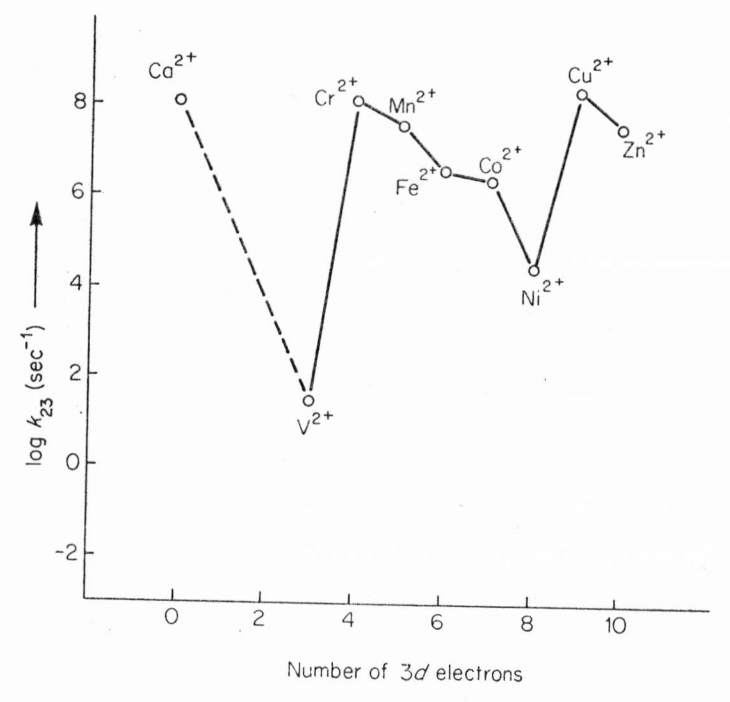

FIGURE 3.9 Variation of water exchange rate for M^{2+} with number of $3d$ electrons. [Data from Ref. 15(c).]

replace the former. The general trend of rates shown in Figure 3.9 is reminiscent of the crystal field stabilization diagrams,[14] but the details have not been satisfactorily explained.

In spite of the uncertainty surrounding the detailed mechanism of metal complex formation, however, the observation that the formation rate constant depends primarily on the nature of the metal is still very important. It implies that large variations in the overall stability constants for different complexes of a given metal are reflected in the rate constant for the *dissociation* rather than the recombination process. This is a very useful result and is rather similar to that obtained for proton-transfer processes. The formation of metal complexes is discussed in greater detail elsewhere.[15]

REFERENCES

1. M. Eigen, *Angew. Chem. Intl. Edn.*, **3,** 1 (1964).
2. M. Eigen, W. Kruse, G. Maass and L. De Maeyer, in *Progress in Reaction Kinetics* (Ed. G. Porter), Vol. 2, Pergamon, London, 1964, p. 286.
3. R. P. Bell, *The Proton in Chemistry*, Methuen, London, 1959, p. 144.
4. (a) E. J. Hart, in *Actions Chimiques et Biologiques des Radiations* (Ed. M. Haissinsky), Vol. 10, Masson et Cie., Paris, 1966, p. 3;
   (b) *Solvated Electron, Adv. Chem. Ser.*, Vol. 50, Am. Chem. Soc., Washington, 1965;
   (c) M. Anbar and P. Neta, *Internat. J. Appl. Radiation Isotopes*, **18,** 493 (1967).
5. E. J. Hart and J. W. Boag, *J. Am. Chem. Soc.*, **84,** 4090 (1962).
6. H. Taube, *Adv. in Inorg. and Radiochem.*, Vol. I, Academic Press, New York, 1959, p. 1.
7. M. Anbar, in Ref. 4(b), p. 55.
8. J. Halpern, *Quart. Rev. (London)*, **15,** 207 (1961); W. L. Reynolds and R. W. Lumry, *Mechanisms of Electron Transfer*, Ronald Press, New York, 1966; A. G. Sykes, *Adv. Inorg. Chem. Radiochem.*, **10,** 153 (1967).
9. M. Anbar and E. J. Hart, *J. Phys. Chem.*, **69,** 973 (1965).
10. G. Stein, in *Hydrogen Bonded Solvent Systems* (Eds. A. K. Covington and P. Jones), Taylor and Francis, London, 1968, p. 94; B. Cercek, *Nature*, **223,** 491 (1969).
11. C. H. Langford and H. B. Gray, *Ligand Substitution Processes*, Benjamin, New York, 1965.
12. R. M. Fuoss, *J. Am. Chem. Soc.*, **80,** 5059 (1958); M. Eigen, *Z. Elektrochem.*, **64,** 115 (1960).
13. D. B. Rorabacher, *Inorg. Chem.*, **5,** 1891 (1966).
14. F. Basolo and R. G. Pearson, *Mechanisms of Inorganic Reactions*, 2nd ed., Wiley, New York, 1967.
15. (a) M. Eigen, *Pure and Appl. Chem.*, **6,** 97 (1963);
   (b) M. Eigen and R. G. Wilkins, in *Mechanisms of Inorganic Reactions, Adv. in Chem. Ser.*, Vol. 49, Am. Chem. Soc., Washington, 1965, p. 55;
   (c) A. McAuley and J. Hill, *Quart. Rev. (London)*, **23,** 18 (1969);
   (d) D. J. Hewkin and R. H. Prince, *Coord. Chem. Rev.*, **5,** 45 (1970).
   (e) D. N. Hague, *Chem. Soc. Spec. Period, Rep.*, No. 18, London, 1971, Part III Charter I.

PROBLEMS

1. Derive expressions for the reciprocal relaxation time associated with the reaction scheme shown in Figure 3.2

   (i) around pH 7,

   (ii) in the range pH 4–10, and

   (iii) at pH <4 and >10.

   [Ref. 1].

2. The deprotonation of acetylacetone may be represented by the reactions

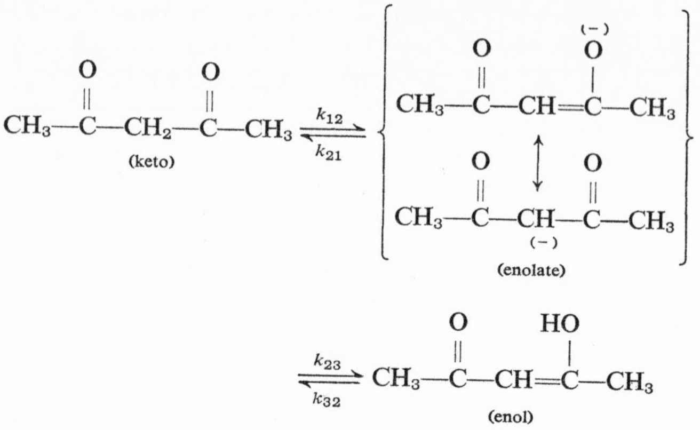

$$\underset{\text{(keto)}}{CH_3{-}\overset{\overset{\large O}{\|}}{C}{-}CH_2{-}\overset{\overset{\large O}{\|}}{C}{-}CH_3} \underset{k_{21}}{\overset{k_{12}}{\rightleftharpoons}} \left\{ \begin{matrix} CH_3{-}\overset{\overset{O}{\|}}{C}{-}CH{=}\overset{\overset{O^{(-)}}{|}}{C}{-}CH_3 \\ \updownarrow \\ CH_3{-}\overset{\overset{O}{\|}}{C}{-}\underset{(-)}{CH}{-}\overset{\overset{O}{\|}}{C}{-}CH_3 \\ \text{(enolate)} \end{matrix} \right\}$$

$$\underset{k_{32}}{\overset{k_{23}}{\rightleftharpoons}} \underset{\text{(enol)}}{CH_3{-}\overset{\overset{O}{\|}}{C}{-}CH{=}\overset{\overset{HO}{|}}{C}{-}CH_3}$$

Predict the values of the four rate constants, giving your reasons. (The pK_a of the enol form is 8·2 and of the keto form 9·0.) [Ref. 2.]

3. Predict the order of decreasing rate constant for the following series of reactions, giving reasons:

(i)
$$M^{2+}_{aq} + SO^{2-}_{4\,aq} \rightarrow MSO_{4\,aq}$$
where M is Be, Mg, Ca, Sr.

(ii)
$$M^{2+}_{aq} + NH_{3\,aq} \rightarrow (MNH_3)^{2+}_{aq}$$
where M is Ni, Cu, Zn.

(iii)
$$Ni^{2+}_{aq} + L_{aq} \rightarrow (NiL)^{2+}_{aq}$$
where L is NH_3, glycinate, oxalate, 5-nitro-*o*-phenanthroline.

(iv)
$$Ni(H_2O)^{2+}_6 + e^-_{aq} \rightarrow Ni(H_2O)^+_6$$
$$Ni(H_2O)^{2+}_6 + H_2O^* \rightarrow Ni(H_2O)_5(H_2O^*)^{2+} + H_2O$$
$$Ni(H_2O)^{2+}_6 + H^+_{aq} \rightarrow Ni(H_2O)_5(H_3O)^{3+}$$

4. In 1966 Rorabacher [*Inorg. Chem.*, **5**, 1891] listed several rate constants for complex formation at Ni^{2+}_{aq}. He found that, if the incoming ligand was bi- or multi-dentate and contained at least one binding group with pK_a greater than that of aquonickel, the rate constant k_f was higher than normal. Suggest an explanation for this in terms of the mechanism discussed on p. 109 (Figure 3.8).

5. Why is it *not* possible to measure the rate of ring-closure when the ultrasonic method is used to follow the reaction of an alkali metal with nitrilotriacetate [M. Eigen and G. Maass, *Z. Phys. Chem. N.F.*, **49**, 163 (1969)] whereas it *is* possible when the pressure-jump method is used to follow the reaction of nickel with malonate [U. Nickel, H. Hoffman and W. Jaenicke, *Ber. Bunsenges. Physik. Chem.*, **72**, 526 (1968)]? In both systems the rate of ring-closure (step b in Figure 3.8) is comparable to the rate of water-substitution (step a).

CHAPTER FOUR

RAPID REACTIONS IN BIOLOGICAL SYSTEMS

Many of the most exciting developments in modern science have involved the application of physical techniques to the problem of explaining the intricacies of living systems in molecular terms. The greatest success so far has been the elucidation in outline of the way in which genetic information is passed on from parent to daughter cell and is used by the cell to construct proteins of particular composition. The note by Watson and Crick[1] to *Nature* in 1953 outlining the double-helical structure of DNA revealed one of the undoubtedly great discoveries in the history of science. X-ray and other physical techniques are being used more and more to complement chemical studies, and the structures of several proteins have now been announced.

A no less important aspect of a biological reaction is its dynamics. An enzyme is a biological catalyst and it therefore alters the kinetics of a reaction rather than its overall thermodynamics. This gives us an overriding reason for investigating the rate of the reaction rather than its equilibrium constant if we are to hope to explain the frequently found high specificity of a particular enzyme. Because most biological reactions are 'instantaneous' it has not been possible to study their kinetics at natural concentrations until the development of the techniques described in Chapter 2, but there is evidence that the application of these techniques to the more complex systems will yield information no less significant than that obtained with simpler reactions (Chapter 3). In this chapter we shall discuss a few of the systems which have already been studied and, because of the novelty of the techniques and the complexity of the reactions, this will be somewhat more tentative than was the case previously. There have been several excellent reviews by Eigen on the application of these techniques, especially chemical relaxation, to biological systems[2] and Hammes has recently reviewed his extensive work with proteins.[3] Although the stopped-flow technique has been applied in several cases, it will not be emphasized here—partly because it is essentially an extension of classical techniques and partly because its application to enzyme and other biological studies has recently been admirably discussed.[4]

ENZYMES

Although the reactions of enzymes are fast, it has been possible to study them kinetically for many years by using very low concentrations. The steady-state treatment dates from 1913 when Michaelis and Menten showed that the rate data could be analysed in terms of a simple two-step sequence involving an intermediate enzyme–substrate complex ES (equation (4.1)),

$$E + S \underset{k_{21}}{\overset{k_{12}}{\rightleftharpoons}} ES \xrightarrow{k_{23}} E + P \tag{4.1}$$

where E represents the enzyme, S the substrate and P the product(s). The rate of formation of ES is given by,

$$\frac{d[ES]}{dt} = k_{12}[E][S] - (k_{21} + k_{23})[ES]$$

and, applying the steady-state hypothesis, is assumed to be zero. Hence,

$$[E] = \frac{[ES](k_{21} + k_{23})}{k_{12}[S]} = \frac{[ES]K_m}{[S]}$$

where $K_m \equiv (k_{21} + k_{23})/k_{12}$ is the so-called Michaelis constant. If the overall enzyme concentration is

$$[E_0] = [ES] + [E]$$

then the overall rate V

$$= \frac{d[P]}{dt} = k_{23}[ES] = \left(\frac{k_{23}[E_0]}{1 + K_m/[S]}\right).$$

At low substrate concentrations (i.e. much less than K_m) the limiting expression for the rate is first order in $[E_0]$ and [S] and at high substrate concentrations (i.e. much greater than K_m) the limiting expression for V is first order in $[E_0]$ and zero order in [S]. Thus a plot of V against [S] at constant overall enzyme concentration has the form shown in Figure 4.1(*a*) which is reminiscent of the rate/pressure plot for unimolecular gas-phase reactions. The region in which the overall order is one corresponds to the situation in which the enzyme is saturated, and the maximum turn-over rate is given by $V_{max} = k_{23}[E_0]$. The two parameters which are derived from steady-state kinetics are therefore K_m and V_{max}, although they are more conveniently obtained from modified Michaelis–Menten plots such as those due to Lineweaver and Burke (Figure 4.1(*b*)) and Woolf and Hofstee (Figure 4.1(*c*)).

What do these parameters tell us? The maximum rate V_{max} evidently refers to the overall process and it can be converted into a true rate constant for the rate-determining step (together with equilibrium constants of fast preequilibria) provided that $[E_0]$ and the number of active sites per enzyme are known. The Michaelis constant K_m is effectively an equilibrium constant since it represents the ratio of the rate constants for the dissociation and formation of the Michaelis complex, i.e. k_{off}/k_{on}. Thus, although

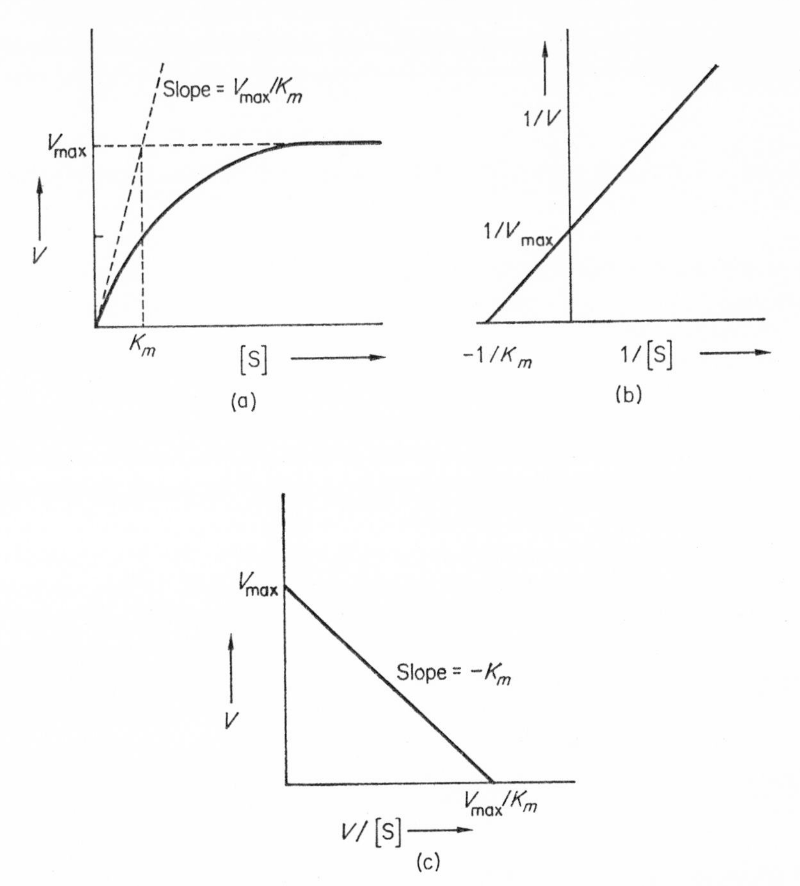

FIGURE 4.1 Steady-state rate of enzyme reaction (*a*) according to Michaelis and Menten, (*b*) according to Lineweaver and Burk, (*c*) according to Woolf and Hofstee. V is the rate and [S] the substrate concentration.

it involves rate constants from the two (hypothetical) steps, it does not contain any direct kinetic information. Even if it were a true equilibrium constant it would not tell us anything about the kinetics of the formation of the Michaelis complex since, as is pointed out below, there is not necessarily any connection between the variation in the rates of formation and dissociation of complexes involving a macromolecule and the variation in the corresponding equilibrium constants.

The scheme represented by equation (4.1) is inevitably deficient in at least two respects. Since enzyme reactions are reversible, the corresponding reaction between E and P (represented by k_{32}) must be considered. (It is actually not important under the conditions usually employed in steady-state investigations since $[S] \gg [P]$.) In addition, it is necessary to include at least one other step, involving the species EP in which the product is bound to the enzyme. Even by making these allowances and conducting the steady-state experiments in both directions (i.e. E + S to give P and E + P to give S, yielding two Michaelis constants and two maximum velocities) it is not possible to obtain kinetic information about all of the steps. In addition, if the reaction sequence involves a complication such as a cooperative conformational change of the enzyme, it is not possible to measure this kinetically (except when it is rate limiting) unless it can be 'seen'—i.e. unless the concentration of the enzyme is stoichiometric rather than catalytic. It would certainly be wrong to suggest that steady-state investigations are worthless—indeed, much invaluable information has been obtained in this way (e.g. by Cleland[5]) and it is sometimes even possible to change the rate-determining step and therefore obtain kinetic information about more than one step—but it is necessary to bear in mind the limitations of the technique.

It is useful to divide the overall reaction into a sequence of elementary steps (see p. 3) and then to discuss the ways in which various factors affect the rates of these elementary processes. Much of the information about the kinetics of the elementary steps has been obtained by studying model systems which are better characterized than the biological systems themselves. It is convenient to suppose that reactions of enzymes involve up to three types of elementary steps, e.g.,

$$E + S \overset{①}{\rightleftharpoons} ES \overset{②}{\rightleftharpoons} E'S \overset{③}{\rightleftharpoons} EP \overset{①}{\rightleftharpoons} E + P$$

where ES and E′S are the enzyme–substrate complex in two different conformations and the other letters have their previous meanings. Reaction ① is the formation and dissociation of a complex (involving diffusion); reaction ② is a rearrangement (conformational change); and reaction ③ is a chemical reaction such as proton transfer or electron transfer. We shall consider steps ① and ② in greater detail below; they are important inasmuch as they provide optimal conditions of alignment, etc., for the actual chemical change (step ③), which involves covalent bond rupture. (Similar considerations apply to the reactions of many other biological macromolecules but the detailed picture may be rather different.)

We have seen in Chapter 3 that for 'normal' acids and bases the forward rate constant is diffusion-controlled (approx. 10^9–10^{11} l/mole sec) if the acceptor binds the proton more strongly than the donor (i.e. it has a higher pK). The reverse rate constant can then be calculated from the difference in the pK values of acceptor and donor (ΔpK) and the forward rate constant. The plots of $\log k$ against ΔpK are therefore straight lines with slope 0 or ± 1 (Figure 3.4). A similar picture is found with C-acids and other poor acceptors except that the forward rate constant is now no longer diffusion-controlled (but often tends to a constant value at sufficiently high values of $|\Delta \text{p}K|$) and so the plots of $\log k$ against ΔpK are gentle curves with slope between 0 and ± 1. It is possible to correlate[6] this behaviour with the Brønsted law for general acid–base catalysis which relates the rate constant k for a catalysed reaction to the pK of the catalyst (pK_c):

$$\log k = \text{constant}\ (\text{p}K_c)^{\alpha}$$

or

$$\log k = \text{constant}\ (\text{p}K_c - \text{p}K_s)^{\alpha}$$

where pK_s is the pK of the substrate. The value of α is usually a constant between 0 and 1 for a particular reaction. The Brönsted relationship was determined by classical means and therefore referred to rate constants corresponding to a relatively narrow range of ΔpK values. It also involved poor acceptors, for which the normal $\log k/\Delta \text{p}K$ transition from ± 1 to 0 occurs over a wide pK range, and so the smooth transition in the slope can usually be approximated to a constant (i.e. α is also equal to the slope of the graph of $\log k$ against ΔpK). The majority of enzyme reactions are sensitive to pH and it is reasonable to suggest that their mechanism involves acid–base catalysis, in which case the principles we have been discussing are equally applicable to the reactions taking place at the active site. As we shall see, it is possible, on this basis, to rationalize the frequent occurrence of the imidazole group of histidine at the active site of hydrolytic enzymes.

General acid–base catalysis involves the transfer of a proton between the enzyme and its substrate, and the subsequent re- or deprotonation of the enzyme in order to return it to its original state. Thus proton transfer is necessary in both directions and the overall half-life is equal to the sum of the two individual half-lives. The process is therefore most efficient if both half-lives are as low as possible (i.e. both rate constants are as high as possible), and this usually occurs where the two $\log k/\Delta \text{p}K$ lines cross—i.e. where $\Delta \text{p}K = 0$. If ΔpK is very different from zero, either the protonation or the hydrolysis rate constant will become very different from its maximum value and so this process will become rate limiting. Since the concentrations of H^+ and OH^- are approximately 10^{-7} M at neutrality, the maximum rate constant of 10^{10}–10^{11} l/mole sec corresponds to a maximum turnover of 10^3–10^4 sec^{-1}. A donor with a pK value of less than 7 could transfer a proton more quickly, but the subsequent hydrolysis would be slower; similarly, a donor with a pK greater than 7 would transfer its proton less readily, although the subsequent hydrolysis would be faster.

This suggests that the maximum turnover of an enzyme involved in proton transfer should be 10^3–10^4 sec^{-1}, but maximum velocities as high as 10^5 sec^{-1} have been observed. This has been rationalized in terms of the *specific* acid–base properties of imidazole. It has been suggested that the proton charge in the hydrogen-bond between two imidazole molecules tends to be delocalized over the two residues, one of which is formally an anion and the other of which is formally a cation (4.2). If this tendency is

```
     H             H
     C             C
   //  \         //  \
  N     N—H·····N     N—H
  |     |       |     |
  HC════CH      HC════CH

                          H                  H
                          C                  C
                        //  \              //  \
                       N    (−)N·····H—N(+)    N—H
                  ⇌    |       |        |      |        (4.2)
                       HC══════CH      HC══════CH
```

sufficiently strong it should have a significant effect on the proton-donating properties of imidazole. This type of argument is supported by the observation that in several acid–base catalysed reactions, imidazole compounds are rather better catalysts than other species with similar pK.

The role of electron transfer in biological systems is rather less clear than that of proton transfer. An interesting summary has been given by Chance[7] of his studies involving electron transfer in cytochromes and biological membranes using flow and Q-switched laser flash techniques.

FORMATION AND DISSOCIATION OF COMPLEXES

In this section we shall consider the formation and dissociation of complexes, such as those between enzyme and substrate, and we shall find that, although the interactions involved are often 'weak' (van der Waals, hydrogen-bonding, etc.), a large degree of specificity can often be introduced into the reaction at this stage.

There have been very few direct kinetic studies on the formation of enzyme–substrate complexes, primarily because the reactions are so fast,

It is always possible to place a lower limit on the rate constant for ES formation from steady-state kinetic studies of the overall enzyme reaction, and it is even possible to obtain an actual value in certain cases. Flow techniques have been employed in systems where the method of detection is sufficiently sensitive to allow low concentrations to be used.[4] Several studies have used chemical relaxation methods and n.m.r., whose shorter time scales are more appropriate than classical and flow techniques. They have also been used to study model systems, such as enzyme-inhibitor and antibody-hapten, which have the advantage of not involving subsequent 'irreversible' reactions.

A few typical rate constants for the formation and dissociation of complexes between proteins and small molecules are given in Table 4.1. It will be seen that all of the formation rate constants are quite large, tending to be in the range 10^6–10^8 l/mole sec. This is rather close to, but usually definitely less than, the limiting diffusion-controlled value (Chapter 1). The dissociation rate constants vary over several orders of magnitude and reflect the varying strength of the interaction between the substrate and protein.

A particularly interesting model system for the enzyme–substrate reaction involves α-cyclodextrin. The cyclodextrins, which are degradation products of starch, comprise various numbers of glucose units joined together in a ring in such a way that hydrophobic groups are concentrated on one side and hydrophilic groups on the other. These compounds form addition complexes with various molecules and α-cyclodextrin, which consists of six glucose units, forms 1:1 compounds with azo-dyes of the type (I). It is thought that the phenyl group of (I) enters the cyclodextrin ring (II) and the two molecules are held in place by hydrogen-bonding,

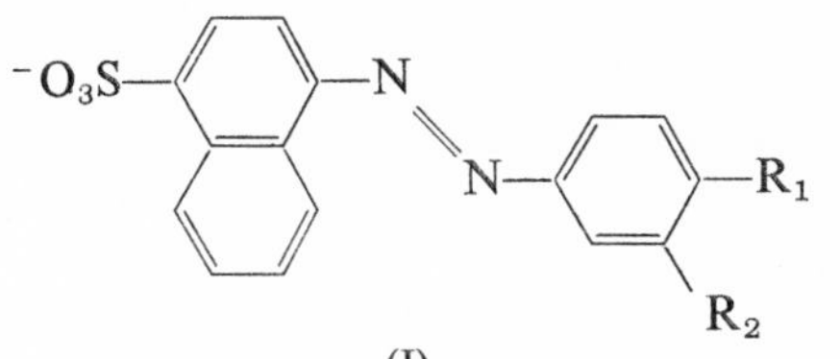

^-O_3S—N=N—R_1, R_2

(I)

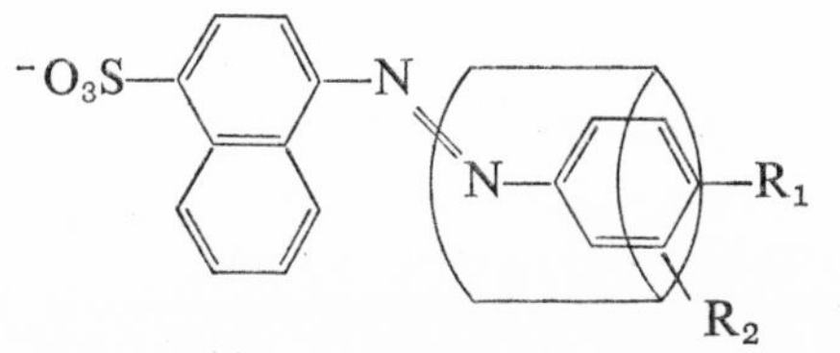

^-O_3S—N=N—R_1, R_2

(II)

TABLE 4.1 Rate constants for the formation (k_f) and dissociation (k_d) of some complexes between macromolecules and small molecules.

Macromolecule	Small molecule	k_f (l/mole sec)	k_b (sec^{-1})	Method	Ref.
acetylcholinesterase	acetylcholine	$>10^9$	—	SS	1
glyceraldehyde-3-phosphate dehydrogenase	NAD	$1{\cdot}9 \times 10^7$	1×10^3	TJ	2
liver alcohol dehydrogenase	NAD	$5{\cdot}3 \times 10^5$	74	SS	1
liver alcohol dehydrogenase	NADH	$1{\cdot}1 \times 10^7$	3·1	SS	1
peroxidase	H_2O_2	9×10^6	$<1{\cdot}4$	F	1
peroxidase	cytochrome c	$1{\cdot}2 \times 10^8$	—	F	1
lysozyme	di-N-acetyl-glucosamine	$4{\cdot}6 \times 10^6$	$9{\cdot}5 \times 10^2$	TJ	3
lysozyme	tri-N-acetyl-glucosamine	$4{\cdot}4 \times 10^6$	28	TJ	3
porcine lactate dehydrogenase	NADH (pH = 6)	$3{\cdot}3 \times 10^6$	32	TJ	4
glutamic-aspartic transaminase (aldehydic)	glutamate	$3{\cdot}3 \times 10^7$	$2{\cdot}8 \times 10^3$	TJ	1
glutamic-aspartic transaminase (aldehydic)	aspartate	$>10^7$	$>5 \times 10^3$	TJ	1
glutamic-aspartic transaminase (aldehydic)	NH_2OH	$3{\cdot}7 \times 10^6$	38	TJ	1
glutamic-aspartic transaminase (aldehydic)	oxalacetate	$>5 \times 10^8$	$>5 \times 10^4$	TJ	1
bacterial alkaline phosphatase (pH = 8)	2-hydroxy-5-nitrobenzyl phosphonate	$2{\cdot}8 \times 10^7$	7×10^3	TJ	5
α-chymotrypsin (pH = 7·6)	Biebrich Scarlet	$2{\cdot}1 \times 10^7$	$6{\cdot}6 \times 10^2$	TJ	6
bovine serum albumin	NR′	2×10^6	35	TJ	1
bovine serum albumin	NSR′	$3{\cdot}5 \times 10^5$	2·5	TJ	1

Various temperatures were used, usually approx. 25°. The techniques used were steady-state (SS), temperature-jump (TJ) and flow (F). The references are:

1. M. Eigen and G. G. Hammes, *Advances in Enzymology*, Vol. 25, Interscience, New York–London, 1963, P.1.
2. K. Kirschner, M. Eigen, R. Bittman and B. Voigt, *Proc. Natl. Acad. Sci. U.S.*, **56**, 1661 (1966).
3. D. M. Chipman and P. R. Schimmel, *J. Biol. Chem.*, **243**, 3771 (1968).
4. H. d'A. Heck, *J. Biol. Chem.*, **244**, 4375 (1969).
5. H. Gutfreund and S. E. Halford, to be published.
6. D. N. Hague, J. S. Henshaw, V. A. John, M. J. Pooley and P. B. Chock, *Nature*, **229**, 190, (1971).

van der Waals forces and hydrophobic bonding. (These complexes are analogues of the blue starch–iodine complex.)

The kinetic and thermodynamic data[8] for several of these compounds are shown in Table 4.2. Although the equilibrium constants are essentially invariant for the series, the rate constants for formation and dissociation vary over more than seven orders of magnitude. This is therefore an example of a series of related reactions which are not differentiated thermodynamically, but for which there is a very large kinetic discrimination. It also emphasizes the danger of drawing conclusions about the individual rate constants from an observed constancy in equilibrium or pseudo-equilibrium constants, such as the Michaelis constant K_m, for a series of related reactions.

In the example we have just considered, the specificity was introduced into the reaction of the macromolecule by steric means. Another way of introducing kinetic discrimination into a biological system is by the use of a metal ion.

METALS IN BIOLOGY

Metals play a very important role in biological systems and they may be classified into three groups:

(i) Those involved in redox systems, such as Fe in the cytochromes, Cu in the 'copper blue' enzymes and Co in vitamin B_{12};

(ii) Those which are not involved in redox systems and in which the metal is not directly involved at the site of the reaction. This group contains those enzyme systems in which the metal is bound at some point distant from the active site and may be there to maintain a certain conformation or to polarize bonds which are then involved in the reaction. The metal may, in fact, be acting as a convenient source of a multiple positive charge. This group probably includes Mg^{2+}, Mn^{2+} or Ca^{2+} in creatine kinase;

(iii) Those which are not involved in a redox system but in which the metal is directly involved in the reaction. We shall be concerned only with this group, which includes those systems in which the metal ion binds to an enzyme at its active site and acts as a bridge between enzyme and substrate (e.g. Zn^{2+} in carbonic anhydrase and Mg^{2+} in pyruvate kinase). Metal complex formation and dissociation are important aspects of the overall mechanism. (This classification is somewhat different from the frequently used one of 'metallo-enzyme', in which the metal cannot easily be removed from the enzyme, and 'metal-activated enzyme', in which it can; it has the advantage of grouping the systems according to mechanism. Metal complex formation is also important in several redox systems.)

TABLE 4.2 Rate constants for the formation (k_f) and dissociation (k_d), and dissociation constants (K_D) for the inclusion compounds between azo dyes and α-cyclodextrin* in water (at 14°C).

Substrate	k_f (l/mole sec)	k_d (sec^{-1})	K_D (mole/l)
$^{-}O-C_{10}H_5(SO_3^{-})-N{=}N-C_6H_4-NO_2$	$5{\cdot}2 \times 10^7$	$1{\cdot}3 \times 10^5$	$3{\cdot}2 \times 10^{-3}$
$R-N{=}N-C_6H_4-OH$	$1{\cdot}3 \times 10^7$	$5{\cdot}5 \times 10^4$	$3{\cdot}7 \times 10^{-3}$
$R-N{=}N-C_6H_4-O^-$	$1{\cdot}7 \times 10^5$	$2{\cdot}6 \times 10^2$	$1{\cdot}55 \times 10^{-3}$
$R-N{=}N-C_6H_4-N(CH_3)_2$	$1{\cdot}1 \times 10^6$	1×10^3	$0{\cdot}99 \times 10^{-3}$
$R-N{=}N-C_6H_3(CH_3)-OH$	$1{\cdot}2 \times 10^5$	$3{\cdot}5 \times 10^2$	$2{\cdot}4 \times 10^{-3}$
$R-N{=}N-C_6H_3(CH_3)-O^-$	$1{\cdot}5 \times 10^2$	0·28	$2{\cdot}1 \times 10^{-3}$
$R-N{=}N-C_6H_3(CH_2CH_3)-OH$	6×10^3	19	$2{\cdot}2 \times 10^{-3}$
$R-N{=}N-C_6H_3(CH_2CH_3)-O^-$	2·8	1×10^{-2}	$3{\cdot}5 \times 10^{-3}$

$R = {}^{-}O_3S-C_{10}H_6-$

Kinetic and equilibrium values were determined independently.

* Data from Ref. 8.

In some cases the requirement for a metal ion is general but in many the metal specificity is very nearly absolute. In order to achieve high turnover numbers, the stability constants of the active metal complexes tend to be low (the metals are either low in the Irving–Williams series or the substrate is monodentate), and the rate constants tend to be high—the ideal situation for the application of relaxation techniques. We shall discuss two systems in which the metal specificity is high and where this can be rationalized in kinetic terms, though it must be emphasized that the conclusions are based on the study of model systems only.

Many biological membranes are thought to consist of a double layer of lipid molecules arranged so that their polar groups, together with protein molecules, are on the outside and their hydrophobic chains are on the inside (Figure 4.2). Although they are often somewhat more complex than this, nerve membranes are rather similar. Nerve action is associated with the selective passage through the membrane of the alkali metals Na^+ and K^+ (and, indeed, this selectivity appears to be important in other cells). In the resting state the fluid inside the nerve is negatively charged relative to that outside and the passage of the impulse along the nerve axon is associated with the sudden reversal of this potential difference. The resting potential (of the order of 50 mV) is caused by different concentrations of several ions on the inside and outside including sodium (approximately 50 and 450 mM, respectively) and potassium (400 and 20 mM). The high external concentration of Na^+ and internal concentration of K^+ (which is also found in other cells) is brought about by the 'sodium pump' whereby Na^+ ions are continuously removed from the inside fluid against the concentration gradient. Thus there is a very efficient recognition by the membrane of Na^+ in the presence of K^+. It has been pointed out on p. 110 that this selectivity seems feasible on the basis of the kinetics of complex formation and dissociation with model systems. The discrimination between Na^+ and K^+ in terms of the dissociation rate constants for complexes

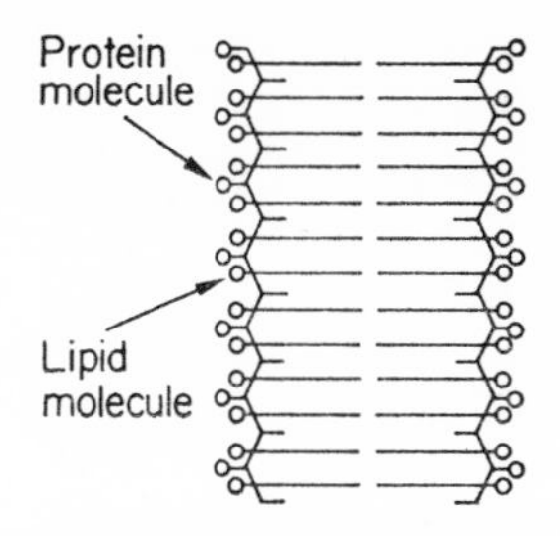

FIGURE 4.2 Model of cell membrane (Danielli).

with multidentate ligands, such as nitrilotriacetate and uramildiacetate, is high and the half-life for the sodium complex is comparable to the time taken for the complex to diffuse through 100 Å, the thickness of the membrane, while that for the potassium complex is much less. This is only a model (the effect of the hydrocarbon medium on the dissociation rate of the complex is not taken into consideration), but it again illustrates the way in which kinetic discrimination might be applied.

An interesting development of this idea concerns the action of various antibiotics and 'crown' poly-ethers. Some of these compounds, such as valinomycin, dinactin, enniatin, have been found to make various biomembranes selectively porous to different alkali metals. It has been shown that several of these macromolecules form complexes with alkali metals in which the metal ion is surrounded by polar groups while the outside of the complex is hydrophobic (e.g. Figure 4.3). These compounds can change

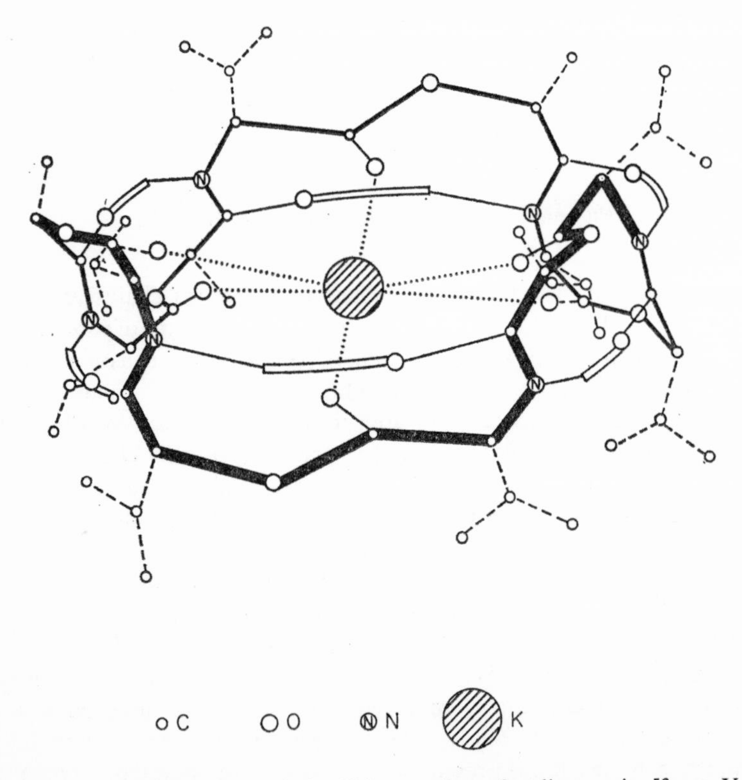

FIGURE 4.3 Conformation of the K^+ complex of valinomycin [from V. T. Ivanov, I. A. Laine, N. D. Abdulaev, L. B. Senyavina, E. M. Popov, Yu. A. Orchinnikov and M. M. Shemyakin, *Biochem. Biophys. Res. Comm.*, **34**, 803 (1969)].

conformation so as to eject the metal ion from the centre and it has been suggested that they can discriminate between the alkali metals in the way outlined above: the metal only passes through the membrane when it is inside the macromolecule (hydrophobic groups on the outside), whereas the stable conformation of the latter in water is that in which the hydrophilic groups are on the outside; the lifetime of the complex is determined by the dissociation rate constant. In support of this, it has recently been shown[9] that the forward rate constants for the reaction of the alkali metals with several of these macromolecules are still essentially diffusion-controlled (see p. 110), despite the complexity of the ligands.

The roles of calcium, magnesium and manganese in enzyme reactions, where it is thought that they often form ternary complexes of the type EMS, are somewhat curious. (It should be pointed out, however, that these metal ions do not appear invariably to form active ternary complexes in which the metal acts as a bridge between E and S.) Ca^{2+} and Mg^{2+} are chemically similar and tend to form complexes with bi- and terdentate ligands which have similar stability constants (those with Mg^{2+} often being slightly higher) whereas Mn^{2+}, being a transition element, is rather different chemically and tends to form complexes with stability constants which are two or three orders of magnitude higher. Nonetheless, it is often found that Mg^{2+} and Ca^{2+} are antagonistic towards each other and Mg^{2+} can be replaced *in vitro* by Mn^{2+}.

If we consider the scheme (4.3),

$$\begin{array}{ccccccc} EM + S & \rightleftharpoons & EMS & \rightleftharpoons & EMP & \rightleftharpoons & EM + P \\ & & \updownarrow & & \updownarrow & & \\ & & & (EMS)' & & & \end{array} \qquad (4.3)$$

in which an internal rearrangement to (EMS)′ may or may not be necessary and which can only take place when the metal is actually present on the enzyme, then if such an internal rearrangement is *not* necessary the product will be formed more rapidly when M is Ca^{2+} than Mg^{2+} (since the formation and dissociation rate constants for Ca^{2+} will be higher than those for Mg^{2+}; see Table 3.5). If such a rearrangement *is* necessary, then it will only be possible if the lifetime of the complex is greater than the time necessary for the rearrangement. Typical enzyme turnover numbers are 10^2–10^3 sec^{-1} and this condition is likely to be fulfilled for Mg^{2+} when the stability constant of the complex is greater than approx. 10^3 M^{-1}, but for Ca^{2+} the corresponding stability constant would have to be greater than approx. 5×10^5 M^{-1}, which is very unlikely. By comparison, the formation rate constant for a Mn^{2+} complex is typically 10^2–10^3 times higher than for a Mg^{2+} complex and so, if the stability constants of the two complexes are also in the ratio 10^2–10^3:1, the dissociation rate constants and therefore the lifetimes of the complexes are about the same. Consequently, if a rearrangement is not necessary, Ca^{2+} will be more efficient than Mg^{2+} or Mn^{2+}, but if one is necessary, Mg^{2+} and Mn^{2+} will be more efficient than Ca^{2+}.

The validity of this scheme requires that the effect of one ligand on the rates of complex formation and dissociation of the metal with the other ligand be very small, since the figures we have used are based on data obtained with 1:1 complexes. It has recently been shown[10] for Mg^{2+}, Mn^{2+} and Ca^{2+} that, if the incoming ligand is the bidentate oxinate anion

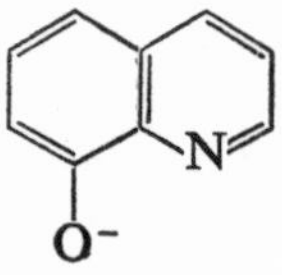

(III)

(III), the effect of another ligand already bound to the metal ion is minimal (Table 4.3). In particular, there is no large decrease in association rate constant (except possibly for Mn^{2+} bound in polyphosphates) or increase in dissociation rate constant when some of the water molecules are substituted by bulky, negatively charged groups. (The Ca^{2+} reactions were too fast to measure with the T-jump, but the same conclusion can be drawn.) Thus it seems that, at least for these electronically symmetrical metal ions, the important factor in determining rates of complex formation and dissociation is the local charge density rather than the overall charge

TABLE 4.3 Rate constants* for the formation (k_f, l/mole sec) and dissociation (k_d, sec^{-1}) of the complex between the oxinate anion and Mg^{2+}—or Mn^{2+}—species in water (at 16°C). The values of k_f have been adjusted to allow for the differing number of available coordination positions.

		M^{2+}	$(M\text{-}UDA)^-$	$(M\text{-}NTA)^-$	$(M\text{-}ATP)^{2-}$	$(M\text{-}TP)^{3-}$
Mg	k_f	$3{\cdot}8 \times 10^5$	$1{\cdot}6 \times 10^5$	—	$1{\cdot}4 \times 10^5$	$0{\cdot}70 \times 10^5$
	k_d	7	41	—	51	6
Mn	k_f	$1{\cdot}1 \times 10^8$	$7{\cdot}2 \times 10^7$	$3{\cdot}8 \times 10^7$	$2{\cdot}0 \times 10^6$	$1{\cdot}2 \times 10^6$
	k_d	140	210	90	35	80

UDA = uramil NN diacetate; NTA = nitrilo triacetate; ATP = adenosine 5′-triphosphate; TP = polytriphosphate.

* Data from Ref. 10.

product and so the discrimination based on k_d is valid also in the more complex biochemical systems.

Another example in which the formation and dissociation of a complex is important involves the complementary base pairing in nucleic acids.

NUCLEIC ACIDS

Although they are based on the repetition of a comparatively simple unit, proteins are complex molecules and are not capable of self-replication. The genetic information which codes for protein synthesis and is passed down from one cell to another is stored in a nucleic acid, usually DNA. The nucleic acids consist of chains of alternating sugar (deoxyribose for DNA and ribose for RNA) and phosphate residues with one of (usually) five organic bases joined to the sugar rings. The bases are the purines adenine (A) and guanine (G), and the pyrimidines cytosine (C), thymine (T, in DNA only) and uracil (U, in RNA only). In DNA two chains, running in opposite directions, usually interact with one another to form a double helix in which bases on one chain are hydrogen-bonded to bases on the other chain. The geometry is such that a purine must interact with a pyrimidine, and it is found that adenine and thymine always pair, as do guanine and cytosine (Figure 4.4). This complementarity provides a very simple scheme for the conversion of a single DNA molecule into two daughters.

In protein synthesis the genetic information corresponding to the amino-acid sequence of the protein is transcribed from the DNA into single-stranded molecules of messenger RNA (mRNA) with the aid of an enzyme, RNA polymerase. mRNA is translated into protein on ribosomes; the amino-acid building blocks are attached to adaptors called transfer RNA (tRNA) and each amino-acid–tRNA unit recognizes its corresponding 'codeword' (or codon) on the mRNA. The codon and its corresponding anticodon consist of three neighbouring purine or pyrimidine bases. (The term codon is used for any 3-base code group and the term anticodon for the complementary unit. Thus the mRNA codons are complementary to and the tRNA codons identical with the DNA codons, with T in the latter replaced by U in the RNAs.) Further enzymes then link the amino-acids together to form the protein. In the self-replication of DNA and in the various transcription stages of protein synthesis the information is passed on by means of a very highly specific hydrogen-bonding between the organic bases. How does this specificity arise, bearing in mind that hydrogen-bonding is possible between all possible pairs of the bases? Evidently an acceptable balance must be achieved between a readout which is slow but sure and one which is rapid but less accurate.

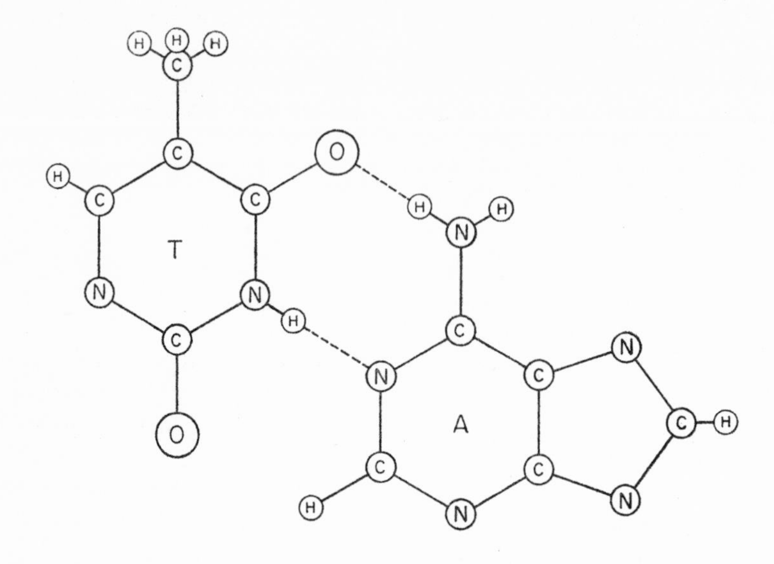

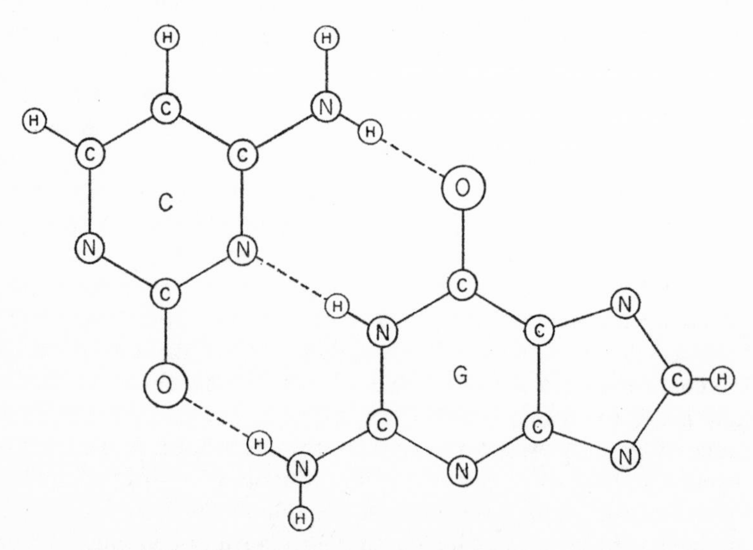

FIGURE 4.4 Hydrogen-bonded base pairing occurring in DNA. In RNA, thymine (T) is replaced by uracil (U).

The pairing of single bases is not possible in water because of the competition for hydrogen-bonding with H_2O molecules. It has, however, been studied in non-polar solvents such as chloroform using the dielectric-loss relaxation method.[11] The single bases have an appreciable dipole moment which is considerably reduced on pairing; consequently, the position of equilibrium depends on the electric field strength. A d.c. field of approximately 200 kV/cm is superimposed on a low amplitude (r.f.) a.c. field, and the absorption of energy is measured as the frequency of the a.c. field is varied. This is a stationary method, see p. 42. It was found that the base-pairing process is very rapid (diffusion-controlled) and that the lifetime of a pair is in the region of 10^{-7} sec. Also, the lifetimes of the different pairs agree with the complementarity—thus, for example, that of an AU pair is greater than that of an AC pair. However, this differential stability of the various pairs is by no means significant enough to account for the low error rate observed in DNA replication. The latter evidently depends also on cooperativity and especially enzyme recognition.

Cooperativity is a very important aspect of the behaviour of nucleic acids (and also proteins) which cannot be investigated with the single bases. The stability of the double-helical structure of DNA depends on the 'stacking interaction' and changes in solvent structure associated with cooperative base pairing. The extent of base pairing can be measured by means of the light absorption at 260 nm since at this wavelength the absorbance of a length of helix is less than that of the corresponding length of random coil. It is found that the helix can be converted into the random coil by heat and that the helix-coil transition ('melting') occurs over a comparatively small temperature range. For simplicity, it is possible to use oligonucleotides of known and differing chain length as a model system for the much more complex DNA (an oligonucleotide consists of a short length of a (base-) sugar-phosphate chain). The increasing extent of cooperativity exhibited by increasing lengths of oligo A is shown in Figure 4.5 and it is apparent that the binding strength per base pair is dependent on the number of base pairs in the oligomer. If it were not, we should expect a general curve describing the temperature-dependence of the binding constant due to a single base pair. Thus, the first base pair is considerably less stable than any subsequent pair, implying that there are different changes in free energy associated with nucleation and propagation. As the chain length is increased further the sharpness of melting also increases and the whole process may be complete within a few degrees. Temperature-jump relaxation studies on oligo A have produced (Ref. 2b) some very interesting results.

When short chains of varying length (the number of bases n being 3 up to approximately 20) of oligo A are either dimerized (at pH $\leqslant 4$) or condensed with chains of oligo U of the same length (at neutral pH) and a temperature-jump applied, a single relaxation is observed for which τ^{-1} varies linearly with concentration of oligomer. This indicates that a simple recombination–dissociation process is involved, and this would be possible in the melting region *only* if the oligonucleotides were present either as single unpaired chains or as completely formed double helices. In other words, all intermediates with less than the maximum number of bases paired must be

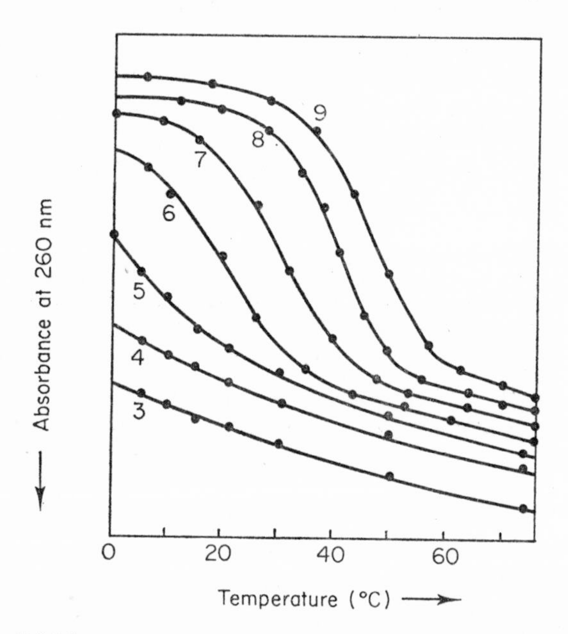

FIGURE 4.5 'Melting curves' for the double stranded oligo-A helices (at pH 4). The melting temperature is that at which the rate of absorbance change is greatest. The numbers of residues per chain are indicated [from Ref. 2(b)].

present at vanishingly small concentration; if this were not so, a spectrum of relaxation times would be observed and this would result in a non-exponential reaction trace. From a suitable plot of τ^{-1} against the concentration of oligomers it is possible to derive the rate constants for the recombination and dissociation processes. The former, k_R, is of the order of 10^6 l/mole sec (rather less than the diffusion-controlled value) and is only very slightly dependent on n for $n > 3$. This suggests that the formation of a nucleus of only three base pairs is sufficient and, once it has formed, the remainder of the helix 'zips up' completely. The dissociation rate constant k_D (approx. 1–10 sec^{-1}) also shows little variation when measured for different values of $n > 3$ at the same degree of helicity (this actually occurs at different temperatures, as indicated in Figure 4.5). The crucial observation concerns the activation energies, as measured by the temperature dependence of the rate constants.

As the temperature is increased, k_D also increases steeply and the corresponding activation energy is proportional to the chain length. Thus it is about 30 kcal/mole for $n = 6$ and increases by 6–7 kcal/mole for each base pair above this. This is not an unexpected result. For the recombination process, however, the rate decreases as the temperature is increased, corresponding to a negative apparent activation energy of down to approximately -20 kcal/mole. This is consistent with the rather low absolute value of k_R and suggests that a preequilibrium is involved, associated with a favourable enthalpy change which outweighs the positive activation enthalpy for the subsequent hydrogen-bonding between base pairs. The interpretation of the recombination rate parameters is that the reforming of the double-helical structure cannot start before a stable nucleus of at least three base pairs has formed. When this has happened the propagation is very fast, being characterized by a rate constant of about 10^7–10^8 base pairs per second.

It is perhaps a little early to extrapolate the conclusions of this work with model systems to DNA itself. It will not have escaped notice that the size of the stable 'nucleus' for the zipping process in the oligonucleotides is about three base pairs, which is the number of bases involved in the codon. It seems that the dynamic stability of a helix of three base pairs strikes a balance between the requirements for a high specificity of recognition (with long lifetime) and speed of scanning (with short lifetime so that many combinations can be tried). Similar processes with DNA itself have been studied by Crothers[12] and others but the fact that one observes a relaxation spectrum makes the interpretation very difficult. Nevertheless it is certain that these studies will be taken further and that they will continue to provide invaluable information about the dynamics of the genetic process.

CONFORMATIONAL CHANGES

One of the most fascinating aspects of enzyme reactions is that it seems that a macromolecule is required for the catalytic action to be really effective. Attempts to produce small molecules which have catalytic activities comparable with those of enzymes have so far been unsuccessful. It appears that the conformation of the protein is of great importance for both recognition and catalysis. Many enzymes also have to exhibit control over the reaction they catalyse and it is thought that this function is connected with the conformational changes which have been shown by o.r.d., and other physical techniques, to take place when substrates and inhibitors bind to some enzymes. Recently, for example, Schwarz has shown[13] that there is a considerable electric-field effect associated with the helix-coil transition in poly (γ-benzyl L-glutamate), a simple protein model. Put another way, this means that the direct action of an electric field, of the order of magnitude of that found across nerve membranes (hundreds of kV/cm), is sufficient to bring about the helix-coil transition. Because of the high cooperatively of the transformation this takes place within a fraction of a microsecond—a result which might have great significance with respect to the action of nerves.

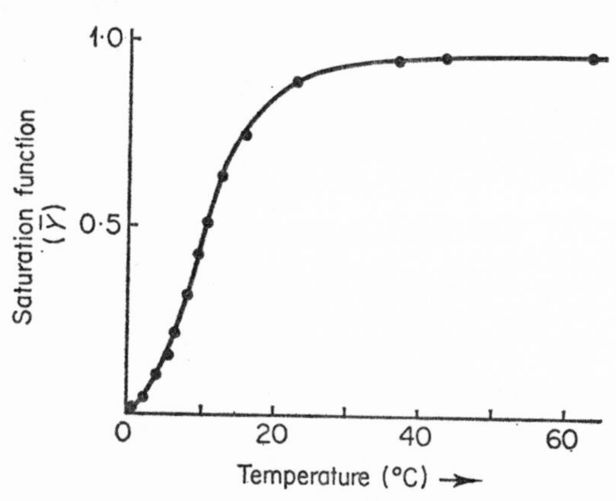

FIGURE 4.6 Saturation of horse haemoglobin (4·6%) with oxygen at 19° and pH 7 (0·6 M phosphate buffer). [Data from R. W. J. Lyster, quoted in Ref. 16.]

Usually, the binding of a substrate to an enzyme is governed by the law of mass action and is characterized by a hyperbolic curve of the type shown in Figure 4.1(*a*) (which has the same shape as plots of steady-state turnover rate and concentration of ES complex against substrate concentration). However, if the enzyme consists of several subunits, each of which can bind, the corresponding plots can become sigmoidal, as shown in Figure 4.6 for the binding of oxygen to haemoglobin. Such a curve is evidence of a cooperativity between the various subunits and indicates that at low substrate concentrations the affinity is relatively low, but at higher concentrations it increases sharply.

Several theories have been put forward to explain this behaviour. In 1925 Adair suggested[14] that a set of four different, successively increasing, binding constants would describe such a sigmoidal curve; but this would only be physically feasible if there were some long-range interaction between the four binding sites (since it would evidently be unreasonable to suggest that the first substrate molecule would bind to any subunit with a lower affinity than that of a subsequent substrate molecule). The X-ray structural data suggest that this is unlikely, at least in the case of haemoglobin. The 'induced-fit' model of Koshland[15] puts this variability of binding constant on a more reasonable physical footing. It supposes that each protein subunit can exist in two conformations; that one is preferred in the absence of the substrate; but that when a substrate molecule binds, the subunit to which it binds changes its conformation (independently of the others). In this new conformation, the subunit has a greater affinity towards substrate molecules and so the subsequent turnovers will occur more efficiently than the first. The scheme is illustrated in Figure 4.7(*a*).

(*a*)

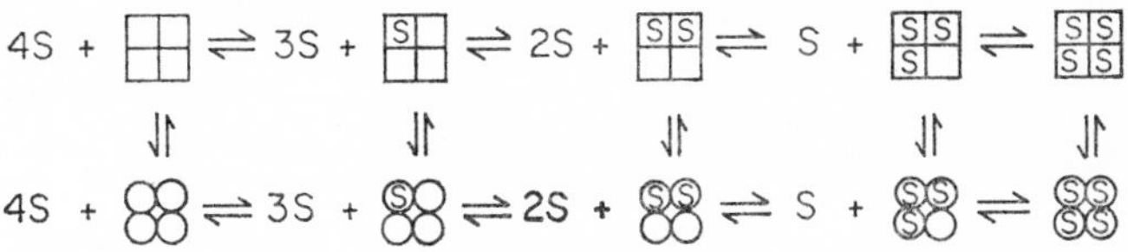

(*b*)

FIGURE 4.7 Reaction schemes for cooperative enzyme action due to (*a*) Koshland, Némethy and Filmer [Ref. 15], and (*b*) Monod, Wyman and Changeux [Ref. 16]. The subunits can be in either of two conformations, represented by □ and ○ (see text).

It leads to the same formal situation as the Adair model but, whereas in the latter the cooperativity results from the difference in the three possible subunit interactions □□, □○ and ○○, in the Koshland model it results from the conformational change.

Monod, Wyman and Changeux[16] proposed a rival 'allosteric' model which, in its restricted form, is represented in Figure 4.7(*b*). It requires fewer parameters than the other schemes, but it also supposes that the two isomeric forms of the enzyme show different affinities towards the substrate. In addition, the four subunits, which are completely degenerate, are either all in one form (the less affine, at low substrate concentration) or all in the other form (the more affine, at high substrate concentration), so that the conformational change is an 'all or none' one of the type we have already observed with oligonucleotides. (Monod's scheme is actually more general than we have outlined and it takes account of the possibility of non-substrate modifiers which convert one form of the enzyme into the other.)

All three models can 'explain' the sigmoidal curves, but they cannot easily be distinguished by equilibrium or steady-state kinetic investigations. By actually seeing and measuring the kinetics of the conformational changes with, for example, relaxation techniques and so separating the various elementary processes along the time axis, it becomes comparatively easy to distinguish between the models. This was possible in the case of the binding of nicotinamide-adenine dinucleotide (NAD) to yeast, D-glyceraldehyde-3-phosphate dehydrogenase (GAPDH), which was studied by the temperature-jump method.[17]

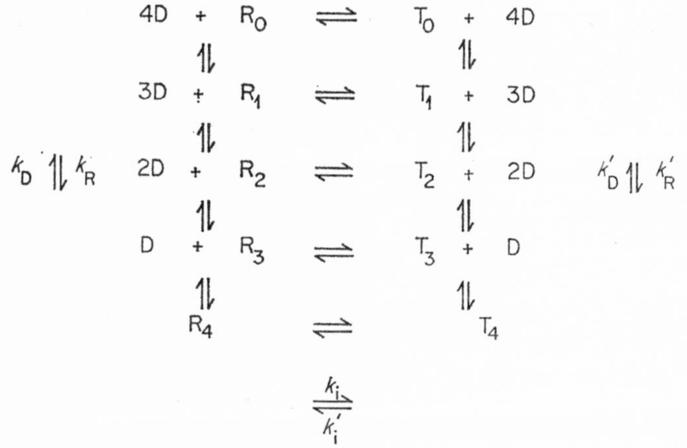

$$
\begin{array}{ccccc}
 & 4D + R_0 & \rightleftharpoons & T_0 + 4D & \\
 & \upharpoonleft\downharpoonright & & \upharpoonleft\downharpoonright & \\
 & 3D + R_1 & \rightleftharpoons & T_1 + 3D & \\
 & \upharpoonleft\downharpoonright & & \upharpoonleft\downharpoonright & \\
k_D \upharpoonleft\downharpoonright k_R & 2D + R_2 & \rightleftharpoons & T_2 + 2D & k'_D \upharpoonleft\downharpoonright k'_R \\
 & \upharpoonleft\downharpoonright & & \upharpoonleft\downharpoonright & \\
 & D + R_3 & \rightleftharpoons & T_3 + D & \\
 & \upharpoonleft\downharpoonright & & \upharpoonleft\downharpoonright & \\
 & R_4 & \rightleftharpoons & T_4 &
\end{array}
$$

$$\underset{k'_i}{\overset{k_i}{\rightleftharpoons}}$$

FIGURE 4.8 Reaction scheme for the binding of NAD to yeast GAPDH (see text).

At about 40° the binding of NAD to GAPDH (which has four subunits, each of which binds one NAD molecule) is weakly sigmoidal and the proposed reaction scheme (cf. Monod) is shown in Figure 4.8. D represents NAD; R_0, R_1, R_2, R_3 and R_4 represent the enzyme in the relaxed (more affine) form with, respectively, 0, 1, 2, 3 or 4 NAD molecules bound; and T_0–T_4 similarly represent the taut (less affine) form of the enzyme. We shall consider the kinetic scheme in some detail because the concentration dependence of the relaxation times was what permitted the distinction between the Monod model and the others.

On submitting the system to a temperature-jump, three relaxation effects were observed, all of which were concentration dependent. They were assigned to the three steps in the Monod scheme as follows:

(i) The fastest (τ_I) represents the binding of NAD to the more affine form R. All values of k_R and k_D, respectively, are equal and, since the conformation of the enzyme is 'frozen in' during this step, we see a simple process of the type $A + B \rightleftharpoons C$ where A is NAD and B is an R-site. The relaxation expression is therefore

$$\tau_{I}^{-1} = k_{D} + k_{R}([D] + \Phi R)$$

where ΦR is the concentration of R-sites

$$(\equiv 4[R_0] + 3[R_4] + 2[R_2] + [R_3])$$

and a suitable plot (Figure 4.9(*a*)) yields values of k_R and k_D.

(ii) The intermediate step (τ_{II}) represents the binding of NAD to the less affine form T. Again the conformation of the enzyme is 'frozen in', but we have to correct for the fast step involving R-sites. The relaxation expression is

$$\tau_{II}^{-1} = k'_{D} + k'_{R}\left\{[D] + \Phi T\left[\frac{[D] + K}{[D] + K + \Phi R}\right]\right\}$$

where ΦT is the concentration of T-sites and K is the equilibrium constant for binding at the R-sites:

$$K = \frac{k_D}{k_R} = \frac{4[R_0][D]}{[R_1]} = \frac{3[R_1][D]}{2[R_2]} = \frac{2[R_2][D]}{3[R_3]} = \frac{[R_3][D]}{4[R_4]}$$

A suitable plot (Figure 4.9(*b*)) yields values of k'_R and k'_D.

(iii) The slowest step (τ_{III}) represents the conformational change of the enzyme, with binding of NAD to R- and T-sites being fast preequilibria. If

$$K' = \frac{k'_D}{k'_R} = \frac{4[T_0][D]}{[T_1]} = \frac{3[T_1][D]}{2[T_2]} = \frac{2[T_2][D]}{3[T_3]} = \frac{[T_3][D]}{4[T_4]}$$

$c = K/K'$, and the 'allosteric constant' L_0 (which is essentially an equilibrium constant) is given by $L_0 = [T_0]/[R_0]$, then the corresponding allosteric constants with various numbers of NAD molecules bound are given by

$$L_1 \equiv [T_1]/[R_1] = c[T_0]/[R_0] = cL_0$$

$$L_2 = c^2L_0$$

$$L_3 = c^3L_0$$

$$L_4 = c^4L_0$$

Now, the observed sigmoidal binding behaviour implies that at very low substrate concentrations the enzyme is present entirely in forms R_0 and T_0 (i.e. there is no bound substrate), while at very high substrate concentrations it is present entirely in forms R_4 and T_4 (i.e. the enzyme is saturated). In each case we would expect a concentration-independent behaviour for τ_{III}^{-1}, but the actual values would be different. It also implies that the T_0

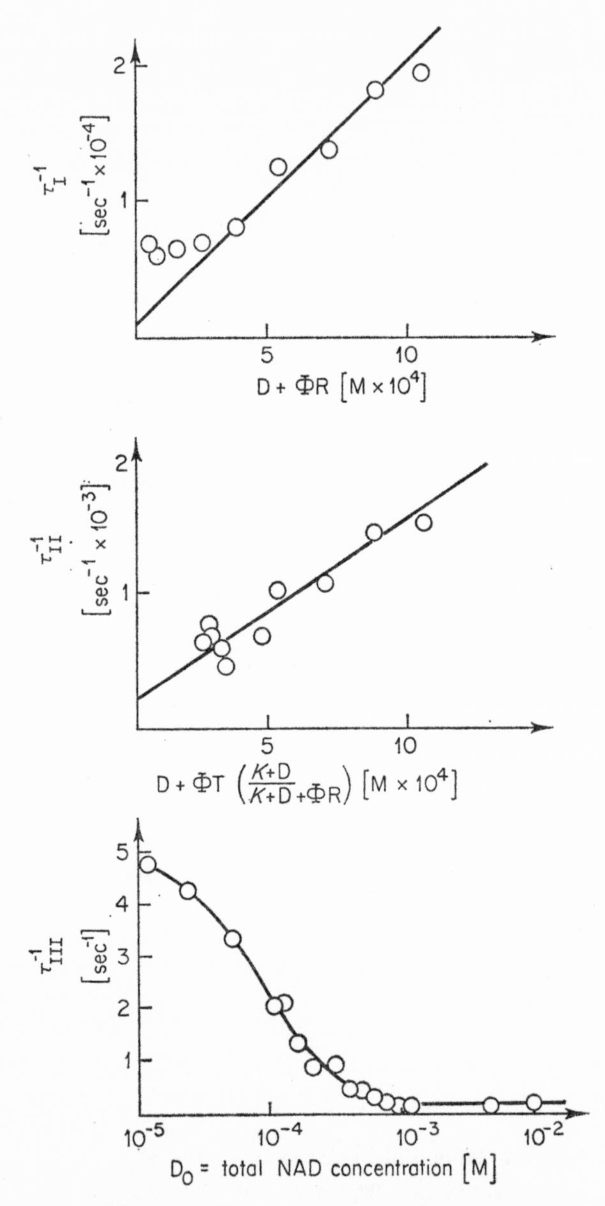

FIGURE 4.9 Dependence of relaxation times on concentration for the binding of NAD to GAPDH (pH 8·5, 40°C) [from Ref. 17].

state must be more stable than the R_0 state, whereas the R_4 state must be more stable than the T_4 state (i.e. $L_0 > 1$ and $L_4 < 1$ or, in other words $L_0 > 1$ and $c < 1$). If we assume that D is quasibuffered and that all values of k_i' are the same, then the expression for τ_{III}^{-1} becomes

$$\tau_{III}^{-1} = k_0' + k_0 \left[\frac{1 + \frac{c[D]}{K}}{1 + \frac{[D]}{K}} \right]^4$$

which leads to the very distinctive concentration dependence shown in Figure 4.9(*c*). As the concentration of NAD is raised to a level where the enzyme begins to saturate, then τ_{III}^{-1} decreases from one constant value $(k_0 + k_0')$ to another $(k_4 + k_4')$. It is lower because of the c^4 relationship between k_4 and k_0 (c being less than 1).

TABLE 4.4 Rate and equilibrium constants* for the binding of NAD to GAPDH (pH 8·5, 40°C) according to the scheme shown in Figure 4.8.

Rate constants	Equilibrium constants
$k_R = 1{\cdot}9 \times 10^7$ l/mole sec; $k_D = 1 \times 10^3\ \text{sec}^{-1}$	$K = 5{\cdot}3 \times 10^{-5}$ M
$k_R' = 1{\cdot}37 \times 10^6$ l/mole sec; $k_D' = 210\ \text{sec}^{-1}$	$K' = 1{\cdot}5 \times 10^{-4}$ M
$k_0 = 5{\cdot}5\ \text{sec}^{-1}$	$c = K/K' = 0{\cdot}35$
$k_0' = k_1' = k_2' = k_3' = k_4' = 0{\cdot}18\ \text{sec}^{-1}$	$L_0 = 30{\cdot}5$
$k_1 = ck_0 = 2{\cdot}0\ \text{sec}^{-1}$	
$k_2 = c^2k_0 = 0{\cdot}7\ \text{sec}^{-1}$	
$k_3 = c^3k_0 = 0{\cdot}24\ \text{sec}^{-1}$	
$k_4 = c^4k_0 = 0.08\ \text{sec}^{-1}$	

* Data from Ref. 17.

In this particular system it was possible to evaluate all the rate constants (Table 4.4), to show that the specific postulates of Monod's model (especially the 'all or none' condition which leads to the distinctive fourth-power concentration dependence for τ_{III}^{-1}) seem to be fulfilled within the limits of experimental error and, in particular, to show that the kinetics are not consistent with the Koshland or Adair model. This does *not* imply, however, that all systems which show sigmoidal behaviour necessarily behave according to Monod's scheme rather than Koshland's and, in fact, Eigen has suggested that the two models might represent the limiting cases of a more general scheme. This aspect of enzyme chemistry is, without a doubt, one of the most exciting areas of present-day scientific research and one in which the application of the modern kinetic techniques we have been discussing will produce many interesting results during the next few years.

REFERENCES

1. J. D. Watson and F. H. C. Crick, *Nature*, **171,** 737 (1953).
2. (a) M. Eigen and G. G. Hammes, *Advances in Enzymology*, Vol. 25, Interscience, New York–London, 1963, p. 1;
   (b) M. Eigen, *Fifth Nobel Symposium, Fast Reactions and Primary Processes in Chemical Kinetics*, Interscience, New York, 1967, p. 333; M. Eigen, in *The Neurosciences* (Eds. G. C. Quarton, T. Melnechuk and F. O. Schmitt), Rockefeller University Press, New York, 1967, p. 130;
   (c) M. Eigen, *Q. Rev. Biophysics*, **1,** 3 (1968).
3. G. G. Hammes, *Advances in Protein Chemistry*, Vol. 23, Academic Press, New York, 1968, p. 1.
4. H. Gutfreund, *An Introduction to the Study of Enzymes*, Blackwells, Oxford, 1965.
5. W. W. Cleland, *Ann. Rev. Biochem.*, **36,** 77 (1967).
6. W. J. Albery, in *Progress in Reaction Kinetics* (Ed. G. Porter), Vol. IV, Pergamon, Oxford, 1967, p. 353.
7. B. Chance, D. deVault, V. Legallais, L. Mela and T. Yonetani, *Fifth Nobel Symposium, Fast Reactions and Primary Processes in Chemical Kinetics*, Interscience, New York, 1967, p. 437.
8. F. Cramer, W. Saenger and H.-Ch. Spatz, *J. Amer. Chem. Soc.*, **89,** 14 (1967).
9. H. Diebler, M. Eigen, G. Ilgenfritz, G. Maass and R. Winkler, *Pure and Appl. Chem.*, **20,** 93 (1969); P. B. Chock and M. Eigen, to be published.
10. D. N. Hague and M. Eigen, *Trans. Faraday Soc.*, **62,** 1236 (1966); D. N. Hague and M. S. Zetter, *Trans. Faraday Soc.*, **66,** 1176 (1970).
11. K. Bergmann, M. Eigen and L. de Maeyer, *Ber. Bunsenges. Physik. Chem.*, **67,** 819 (1963); L. de Maeyer, M. Eigen and J. Suarez, *J. Amer. Chem. Soc.*, **90,** 157 (1968); see also Ref. 2(b).
12. D. M. Crothers, in *The Neurosciences* (Eds. G. C. Quarton, T. Melnechuk and F. O. Schmitt), Rockefeller University Press, New York, 1967, p. 67; H.-Ch. Spatz and D. M. Crothers, *J. Mol. Biol.*, **42,** 191 (1969).
13. G. Schwarz and J. Seelig, *Biopolymers*, **6,** 1263 (1968).
14. G. S. Adair, *J. Biol. Chem.*, **63,** 529 (1925).
15. D. E. Koshland, G. Némethy and D. Filmer, *Biochemistry*, **5,** 365 (1966).
16. J. Monod, J. Wyman and J.-P. Changeux, *J. Mol. Biol.*, **12,** 88 (1965).
17. K. Kirschner, M. Eigen, R. Bittman and B. Voigt, *Proc. Natl. Acad. Sci. U.S.*, **56,** 1661 (1966).

APPENDIX A

TYPICAL REACTION HALF-LIVES AND RATE CONSTANTS WHICH MAY BE DETERMINED BY VARIOUS KINETIC METHODS

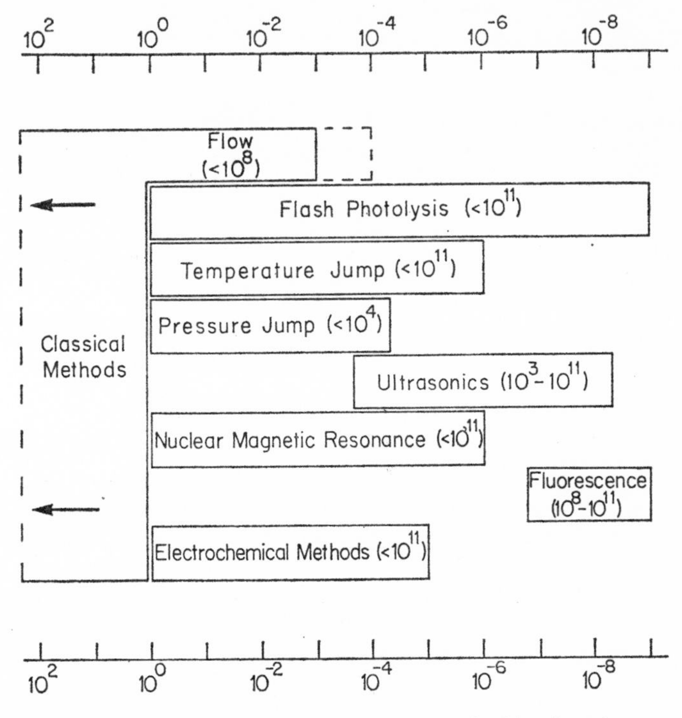

Reaction half-life in sec (rate constant in 1/mole sec).

The ranges of some methods (such as temperature-jump) have been extended into the 'classical' region; these extensions are not noted specifically.

In many respects the typical $t_{\frac{1}{2}}$ accessible by a particular method gives a better impression of its usefulness than the range of second-order rate constants which have been determined. This is because the rate constants which can be measured generally depend to a large extent on such incidental factors as the change in extinction coefficient or enthalpy accompanying the reaction.

APPENDIX B

THE EFFECT OF DIFFUSION ON CHEMICAL KINETICS

The Smoluchowski treatment, based on diffusion down a concentration gradient, leads to an expression for the diffusion-controlled rate constant k_{DC} given by equation (B.1),

$$k_{DC} = 8\pi Da \text{ ml/molecule sec} \tag{B.1}$$

where D is the average diffusion coefficient of the reacting particles A and B and a is the sum of their radii. On the assumption that the motion of molecules in liquids can be represented by the Stokes–Einstein equation, equation (B.2) is obtained for the simple case involving uncharged molecules of the same size,

$$k_{DC} = \frac{8RT}{3000\eta} \text{ l/mole sec} \tag{B.2}$$

where η is the viscosity (see p. 13). This approach has been very successful in predicting the absolute value of k_{DC} and, for example, in predicting the sensitivity of k_{DC} to the viscosity of the solvent and the small variation of k_{DC} with temperature.

Noyes (Ref. 5, Chapter 1) has reviewed critically the development of the theory based on concentration gradients and has pointed out that equation (B.1) represents a limiting case of a more general equation,

$$k_{\text{obs}} = \frac{8\pi Da}{1 + (8\pi Da/k)}$$

where k_{obs} is the observed second-order rate constant and k is the rate constant which would describe the reaction if the equilibrium distribution of molecules were maintained (i.e. if the distribution were not disturbed by the reaction and hence the removal of A and B). It will be seen that if $8\pi Da \ll k$, then $k_{\text{obs}} = k_{DC} = 8\pi Da$ (equation (B.1)), giving a reaction at every encounter. (For small molecules in ordinary solvents, for which the diffusion coefficients are of the order of 10^{-5} cm^2/sec and the intermolecular distances are of the order of 10^{-8} cm, this implies that $k \gg 10^9$ l/mole sec. This condition cannot, however, always be attained even if a reaction does take place at every encounter. Equation (B.1) must therefore be regarded only as an approximation for these reactions.) On the other hand, if $8\pi Da \gg k$ then k_{obs} becomes equal to k and we have classical behaviour. For small molecules in ordinary solvents the effect of the diffusion process on the rate constants will be less than 1% if k is less than 10^7 l/mole sec. For rate constants of 10^8 l/mole sec, the difference between k_{obs} and k is of the order of a few per cent and at 10^9 l/mole sec it is as high as 10%.

In the other approach, based on the behaviour of molecular pairs, an imaginary system containing initially concentrations c_A^0 of A and c_B^0 of B is postulated, and the total distribution of A and B molecules is that predicted by conventional equilibrium statistics. No reactions actually take place in this imaginary system but it is supposed that a 'reaction' has occurred whenever an A and a B molecule get into a situation where they would react if the system were real.

The rate of reaction in the real system is given by,

$$dc_t/dt = k_t(c_A^0 - c_t)(c_B^0 - c_t)$$

where c_t is the number of 'reactions' per unit volume between times 0 and t such that neither the A nor the B molecule involved has previously 'reacted' during this time interval, and k_t is the rate constant applicable at time t. The concentration of 'reacted' A (and also B) molecules is c_t and dc_t/dt is the rate at which the reaction would take place in a real system which was identical to the imaginary system at $t = 0$. In the corresponding imaginary system, there are four additional types of 'reaction' which will not be seen in the real system:

(i) Involving A molecules which have previously 'reacted' at least once and B molecules which have not:

$$\text{rate} = k_t(c_B^0 - c_t)c_t$$

(ii) Involving A molecules which have not 'reacted' but B molecules which have:

$$\text{rate} = k_t(c_A^0 - c_t)c_t$$

(iii) Involving A and B molecules both of which have 'reacted', but not with each other:

$$\text{rate} = k_t c_t^2$$

(iv) Involving A and B molecules which have 'reacted' with each other since $t = 0$.

Suppose $h(t)$ dt is the probability that a pair of molecules in infinite volume which have previously 'reacted' with each other will undergo their first subsequent 'reaction' with each other between t and $t + dt$. Since the total rate of 'reactions' of all types is constant and is equal to $kc^0_A c^0_B$, the rate of these repeating 'reactions' at time t is given by,

$$\int_0^t kc^0_A c^0_B h(t')\,dt'$$

where t' is a time between zero and t.

If the total rate of 'reaction' in the imaginary system is equated to the sum of the rates of all types, the result is

$$kc^0_A c^0_B = k_t(c^0_A - c_t)(c^0_B - c_t) + k_t(c^0_A - c_t)c_t + k_t(c^0_B - c_t)c_t + k_t c_t + kc^0_A c^0_B \int_0^t h(t')\,dt'$$

which may be rearranged to give

$$k_t = k\left[1 - \int_0^t h(t')\,dt'\right]$$

This treatment, as does the other, predicts that a reaction in a real system must be described by an apparent rate constant which is initially equal to that predicted by equilibrium statistics, but which falls rapidly to a lower value as the reaction proceeds.

A further development of the theory of diffusion-controlled reactions is beyond the scope of this book. Noyes, in his admirable review, compares the assumptions used in the two treatments and points out that, although the two arguments are necessarily equivalent, they give different insights into the effects of diffusion on chemical reaction.

APPENDIX C

THE ANALYSIS OF RELAXATION SPECTRA

The mechanisms of many chemical reactions are complex in the sense that they comprise several coupled elementary steps. If there are n independent concentration variables, n independent rate equations will be involved and, if the system is far from equilibrium, it will be extremely difficult to solve them if they include (as they almost certainly will) steps with order greater than unity. By working close to equilibrium, however, all of these rate equations will become linear first-order differential equations of the form

$$-\frac{\mathrm{d}\Delta\bar{c}_i}{\mathrm{d}t} = \sum_{j=1}^{n} a_{ij}\Delta\bar{c}_j \tag{C.1}$$

where the a_{ij}'s are functions of the rate constants and equilibrium concentrations (see p. 35). The rate of change of concentration of a given species i depends not only on the concentration of i but also on the concentrations of other species j.

Such a series of differential equations can be solved conveniently by using matrix algebra.* The system (C.1) can be written in matrix form as

$$-\frac{\mathrm{d}\mathbf{C}(t)}{\mathrm{d}t} = \mathbf{AC}(t) \tag{C.2}$$

where $\mathbf{C}(t)$ is the column matrix

$$\begin{pmatrix} \Delta c_1(t) \\ \Delta c_2(t) \\ \cdot \\ \cdot \\ \cdot \\ \Delta c_n(t) \end{pmatrix}$$

* This problem is considered in most elementary textbooks on matrix algebra, e.g. G. Stephenson, *An Introduction to Matrices, Sets and Groups*, Longmans, London, 1965, Chapter 7.

and **A** is an n by n matrix of the coefficients a_{ij} viz.

$$\begin{pmatrix} a_{11} & a_{12} \cdots & a_{1n} \\ a_{21} & a_{22} \cdots & a_{2n} \\ \cdot & \cdot & \cdot \\ \cdot & \cdot & \cdot \\ \cdot & \cdot & \cdot \\ a_{n1} & \cdots & a_{nn} \end{pmatrix}$$

It may readily be shown that the solution of equation (C.2) is

$$\mathbf{C}(t) = e^{-\mathbf{A}t}\mathbf{C}(0)$$

and the solution of the set of differential equations (C.1) is therefore equivalent to finding $e^{-\mathbf{A}t}$. This may be done in several ways, for example, by diagonalizing the matrix **A**. The solutions λ_j (which are equal to the various reciprocal relaxation times τ_j^{-1}) are the eigenvalues obtained by solving the determinant,

$$\begin{vmatrix} (a_{11} - \lambda) & a_{12} \cdots\cdots & a_{1n} \\ a_{21} & (a_{22} - \lambda) \cdots & a_{2n} \\ \cdot & \cdot & \cdot \\ \cdot & \cdot & \cdot \\ \cdot & \cdot & \cdot \\ a_{n1} \cdots\cdots & \cdots\cdots & (a_{nn} - \lambda) \end{vmatrix} = 0$$

In the comparatively simple case considered on p. 35 the relaxation times are therefore found by solving the determinant

$$\begin{vmatrix} a_{11} - 1/\tau & a_{12} \\ a_{21} & a_{22} - 1/\tau \end{vmatrix} = 0$$

(see p. 36).

The further discussion of this approach for the evaluation of relaxation times is outside the scope of this book; it has been discussed elsewhere (e.g. References 16 and 17 of Chapter 2). As has been pointed out on p. 37, the experimental difficulty of separating individual relaxation times from a relaxation spectrum in which one or more of the other times are similar has tended to limit this type of approach.

APPENDIX D

THE BLOCH EQUATIONS

The Bloch equations represent very well the shape of the n.m.r. absorption line. They may be modified to take account of chemical exchange occurring within the system and an important method for determining rate constants involves the analysis of the modified line shape in terms of these equations.

When a sample is placed in the magnetic field $\mathbf{H}_0$, a magnetization is induced in the material which may be described by a vector **M**. The observed n.m.r. spectrum is determined by the motion of **M** under the influence of the applied r.f. field H_1, and the Bloch equations are a set of three differential equations which give the variation with time of the three components of $\mathbf{M}$: M_x, M_y and M_z (axes as in Figure 2.17 p. 49). The contributions of the precession of the spin system to the time variation of the components of magnetization are:

$$\frac{\mathrm{d}M_x}{\mathrm{d}t} = \omega_0 M_y; \qquad \frac{\mathrm{d}M_y}{\mathrm{d}t} = -\omega_0 M_x; \qquad \frac{\mathrm{d}M_z}{\mathrm{d}t} = 0$$

where ω_0 is the nuclear resonance frequency $= \gamma_N H_0$ (with suitably adjusted units), and the contributions of the relaxation are:

$$\frac{\mathrm{d}M_x}{\mathrm{d}t} = \frac{-M_x}{T_2}; \qquad \frac{\mathrm{d}M_y}{\mathrm{d}t} = \frac{-M_y}{T_2}; \qquad \frac{\mathrm{d}M_z}{\mathrm{d}t} = \frac{-(M_z - M_0)}{T_1}$$

where M_0 is the equilibrium value of the magnetization in the z direction (in the x and y directions the equilibrium values of the magnetization are zero). These are combined to give

$$\frac{\mathrm{d}M_x}{\mathrm{d}t} = \omega_0 M_y - \frac{M_x}{T_2}$$

$$\frac{\mathrm{d}M_y}{\mathrm{d}t} = -\omega_0 M_x - \frac{M_y}{T_2}$$

$$\frac{\mathrm{d}M_z}{\mathrm{d}t} = \frac{-(M_z - M_0)}{T_1}$$

The Bloch equations are, however, usually written in terms of the field axis z and two new axes which rotate about the z axis in the xy plane with an angular velocity equal to that of H_1, i.e. ω. The variables u and v are then the transverse components of magnetization which are, respectively, in-phase (real part) and 90° out-of-phase (imaginary part) with H_1:

$$\frac{\mathrm{d}u}{\mathrm{d}t} = (\omega_0 - \omega)v - \frac{u}{T_2}$$

$$\frac{\mathrm{d}v}{\mathrm{d}t} = -(\omega_0 - \omega)u + \gamma_N H_1 M_z - \frac{v}{T_2}$$

$$\frac{\mathrm{d}M_z}{\mathrm{d}t} = -\gamma_N H_1 v - \left(\frac{M_z - M_0}{T_1}\right)$$

When the r.f. field has been on for a long time the spin precession achieves a steady state; this is represented by the stationary solution of these equations:

$$u = M_0 \left[\frac{\gamma_N H_1 T_2^2(\omega_0 - \omega)}{1 + T_2^2(\omega_0 - \omega)^2 + \gamma_N^2 H_1^2 T_1 T_2}\right]$$

$$v = M_0 \left[\frac{\gamma_N H_1 T_2}{1 + T_2^2(\omega_0 - \omega)^2 + \gamma_N^2 H_1^2 T_1 T_2}\right]$$

$$M_z = M_0 \left[\frac{1 + T_2^2(\omega_0 - \omega)^2}{1 + T_2^2(\omega_0 - \omega)^2 + \gamma_N^2 H_1^2 T_1 T_2}\right]$$

In a normal n.m.r. experiment, the spectrometer is tuned to observe the out-of-phase component v although the in-phase component u is sometimes

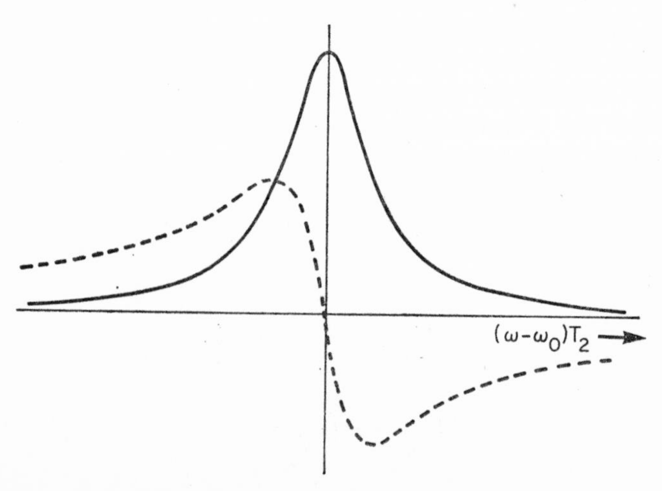

FIGURE A.1 Absorption (full line) and dispersion (dashed line) line shapes predicted by the Bloch equations.

observed (giving a dispersion spectrum rather than an absorption spectrum—cf. the ultrasonic chemical relaxation method discussed on p. 43). If the resonance is unsaturated (p. 51) we can neglect the term $\gamma_N^2 H_1^2 T_1 T_2$ and the shapes of the v-mode (absorption) and u-mode (dispersion) signals are as shown in Figure A.1. The line shapes predicted by the Bloch equations are known as Lorentzian and are characteristic of a damped oscillatory motion. Although a more detailed discussion of these matters is outside the scope of this book, it might be noted that the dispersion and derivative spectra associated with the Lorentz line are not identical; in the dispersion spectrum the separation between peak and trough is equal to $1/(\pi T_2)$ whereas in the derivative spectrum it is equal to $2/(\sqrt{3}T_2)$; cf. Ref. 23 in Chapter 2.

INDEX

QM Library
23 1284220 X